Published June 2021. Second Edition 2022.

ISBN-13: 978-1-7372921-0-4

Published by Courtney Diddell.

info@hellosweetspirit.com

https://hellosweetspirit.com/

Table of Contents

Introduction

She moves through the still desert canyon with practically nothing, wearing just her skirt and tank top. A scarf covers her shoulders and shades her face, protecting her from the desert's blazing sun and brisk nights. Her feet are bare.

A colorful sack made of ancient textiles from the Hmong tribe (a keepsake from her pre-pandemic travels), decorated with jingling bells that bring her back to awareness with each chime, hangs from her shoulders. She calls it "The Magic Bag," because it holds many treasures from her journey, like toys, instruments, and nature's gifts.

She was 22-years-old when Life, the universal experience, began to change dramatically. A virus took over the billions of people spread across the Earth, seemingly under control at first, but never extinguished. Like the wildfires of the West, the virus spread rapidly from community to community, until more than seven billion people rest in peace. No more media, no more medical facilities, and no more jobs the adolescents once dreamt of obtaining.

By 23, she was on her own, with no family or friends—at least that she knew of, since all methods of communication had shut off. As if Life was predetermined by her past-life experiences, she knew the life of a gypsy long before the incident.

Her angelic ambience, floating through life with a contagious calmness and desire to help others, is nothing short of attractive. She possesses the determination to heal, and she often finds her Self with distraught individuals seeking her attention, guidance, or healing.

As she meets these wounded souls along her journey, she finds they all have one thing in common: an intention to understand why they, collectively and individually, survived such a catastrophe.

Through assisting others, she can access the power to heal her Self by drawing connections between every past and present experience, traveling through dreams and her perceived reality, and expanding the perspective of Self and how it reflects into every aspect of Life.

Part 1

Creating Space

The sun is high in the sky, nearly directly above her, absorbing all the shadows, her skin covered by the shadow of her purple silk scarf. She walks slowly to mindfully absorb Life's most unnoticed moments around her, like the small insects clinging to the bottom of sage leaves.

She wanders in a slithering trail, moving forward from one side of the canyon to the other, while observing the rocks beneath her. A river once flooded this channel, and she becomes aware of the Truth. All rocks will crumble into many particles before regrouping as the river deposits these fragments. This means every type of rock she was tested on in geology is not actually limestone or volcanic, but a combination of many varieties—something beyond a human's adopted knowledge. She laughs to her Self and says aloud, "Oh, how near-sighted we humans can be."

Seems like only days ago she set out on this journey but, in her growing desire to walk, she does not realize how many months have actually passed. She dreamt last evening she stumbled across a river party, a Hispanic family celebrating a holiday or maybe the sunshine. Papa sat by the water with his Corona, while the entire population withdrew to their homes in fear of the virus. The concept "my home" makes her smirk, because ownership of a home is no different from saying, "my child," or "my lover," which come and go like the wind, illusive by nature. Homes, post-pandemic, now belong to no one and everyone. Perhaps they always did. She avoided the family's stares and found a hidden space down the river, when she woke up from the dream.

Now, mid-afternoon, two figures are forming in the distance. This is no dream. It always makes her uncomfortable to pass men in this desolation. Who will hear her scream? She veers to the left wall and begins visualizing a bubble around her as she walks. "My space," she whispers and thanks the sandy grounds with every step for the energy rising through her bare feet, feeding her force shield.

The figures slowly approach along the right wall, a boy and his dad. She unforgivably surveys them walking, observing what they wear, what they carry, and the characters they play, with no intention to divert her gaze. Staring comes naturally these days, as she no longer lives by the blinding constraints of manners. They pass by, daddy never gazing at her, and the boy discreetly glancing over, nervous to make contact but as curious as she is. He has long blonde hair and carries a stick to draw copies of his imagination in the dirt—pictures of a mother holding her child.

Without a word, they pass and carry on their way. Her favorite part now begins. Her imagination runs wild with stories and possibilities—what could have happened in the intersection of two paths—as she moves forward on her journey. She is careful to only pay attention to the ones which serve her intention and survival—her highest good—those that do not manifest trouble with strangers. No sense cluttering her space.

Ask your Self, "What's feeding my imagination? Do I experience it coming to life?"

attachment

if Life has
no meaning,
it becomes the game
of reason.
having children, beliefs in religion or philosophy,
a successful job, + education all give Life reason...
what's yours?

are
you
living
for your
reason
or someone
else's?

are you a sun person?

every day, for 9 months,
or 44 minutes, add
10 seconds to your
sungazing practice.
Only sungaze in the
first hour of sunrise
+ the last hour
before sunset.

SUNGAZING

3 months // 15 minutes
-¦- positive thinking; rid
   fear, anger, greed, jealousy
-¦- increased intuition,
   less doubt

6 months // 30 minutes
-¦- rid physical ailments

7.5 months // 35 minutes
-¦- hunger decreases

9 months // 44 minutes
-¦- hunger disappears
-¦- high levels of
   energy

GROUNDING

complete your sungazing practice
barefoot. After 44 minutes, continue
walking barefoot for 45 minutes
daily to continue enhancing immunity
+ expanding the pineal gland

by putting your barefeet, hands,
or body to the Earth (or a tree)
the electrical currents always
existing can boost the immune
system, relieve chronic pain, +
restore the body to its natural
state of being

She

The sun is setting behind the canyon peaks, hinting at traces of rainbow fusions. Her mind is colorful from the desert spring life: insects as large as her thumb burying into the sand, branches and flowers dancing to the song of the wind, gradients of desert hues running up the canyon walls, held together by the roots grasping the mud.

It still concerns her that she finds so much enjoyment in solitude. Occasionally her mind will wander away from her and she will realize the deep slurry she creates around craving and longing for meaningful interaction. Hours of meditative practices each day seem to reduce the duration her mind wanders.

With so much time—or no "time" at all—she meditates more than she sleeps. It dawned on her that survival requires awareness, and sleep offers a lot of unconscious time. Illusion. To give her body adequate rest, she sleeps deeply for two hours, then meditates until the sun rises.

She learned to love the Sun in a way she never could, understanding deeper the necessities it provides. Breakfast or dinner are exchanged with the Sun. She never eats food and can go longer without water, all because the sun offers the most essential nutrients and provides the strongest energy source directly to the third eye.

As the sun makes its hourly descent, she stands barefoot in the dirt, pupils directly pointed toward the ball of light and warmth. She feels the electrical currents race down her back to her toes and fingertips. Forty-five minutes of uninterrupted focus engulf her, and she can see the bubble surrounding her light up, today's final dose of yellow and orange.

As the darkness rises, she moves to the trees for meditation. Her senses have become much more powerful since the pandemic, allowing her to smell, see, and hear predators, but she prefers the safety and comfort of the hardy Juniper trees anyway.

Meditation is an art, rather than a science, and sometimes she does not get the same results. Her mindful focus slips away from her until she sees the man, the boy, and an army of men.

Without a name or relationships, how would you define your Self?

7

Asleep

She moves quietly through the dark, slipping between the trees; this is not her first time on the run. Her breath is quiet and her steps carry her as if she is floating, but they are fast, her endurance strong.

A branch pops up from the dirt, and she hurdles it. As she soars slow motion through the air, her ego inflates at her unexpected abilities, but comes crashing down as one heel hits the wood with a loud crack.

"There she is!" a male voice shouts behind her.

"Welcome to Life," she says, picking up the branch's end with one quick scoop, spinning full circle to slice across the man's face behind her and throwing the branch in the same direction. She does not wait to see him fall; she turns and takes off again.

"I am awake now."

In this life, she has no limits. Being connected with everything around her enables an abundant flow of nature's forces: strength from the thick branch, endurance from the Earth, adrenaline from the sun, stability from the trees. She is free.

The men dissipate behind her, falling off one by one into the lingering darkness. She craves shelter and a place to regroup, when suddenly an abandoned ranch appears under the moonlit sky. "My space," she whispers.

She enters the door, expecting a quiet and empty home. The door swings open to reveal the vast desert night, a house with one wall, and she smirks at Life's quite literal sense of humor. She slows to a walk, returning to observation, finding peace of mind through excellent night vision. She much prefers the Sun, but she holds a strong affair with the Moon.

She sits by a tree and gazes up at Him. The Moon controls her more than she likes to accept, but when the mind's eye is awake, they see eye-to-eye, for He is always awake, and only reflects back to her what she looks up at Him with. Tonight, she feels vibrant and bold, like He is complete, full of light from the Sun.

The tree's roots tuck her in and she begins to focus on the rise and fall of her chest, returning it back to its steady pace. She separates from the body and mind and, floating into the night sky, she looks down at herself from the outside. Silence can be relaxing, especially with a trusted friend.

Describe the feeling of being "awake". What are you "waking up" to?

or are you a moon person?

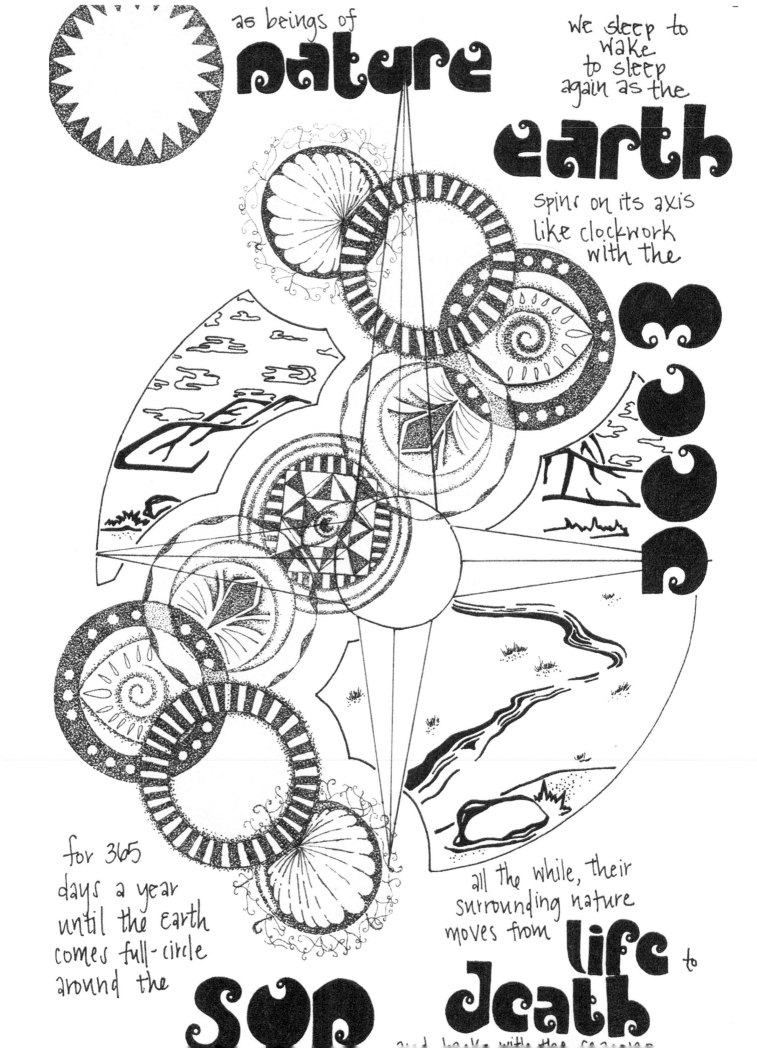

as beings of **nature**

we sleep to wake to sleep again as the **earth**

spins on its axis like clockwork with the **moon**

for 365 days a year until the earth comes full-circle around the **sun**

all the while, their surrounding nature moves from **life** to **death**

Cyclic

She opens her eyes slowly as the sun begins to rise, and crawls out of meditation.

Today she intends to reach the trading post. Despite everyone's fear about the spread of illness, what would be the remaining Americans—if borders still existed—have designated meeting points around the desert for trade. Take what you need—a water jug, exotic foods, building supplies—and move on.

It is always uncertain what will be there, if anything, but people trek long ways for these gatherings in hopes their needs for survival will be met. Trading posts are not about materialism for her, but rather a chance to reveal her newest additions to the Magic Bag in exchange for a smile or a laugh.

She climbs up a sloping canyon wall to see if she can spot the meeting point, a cluster of massive boulders hiding ancient cliff dwellings centuries old. Her internal GPS never fails her, as she just listens to the inner guidance: "Take the coyote trail behind that cactus. Follow the direction of those wings. Turn right where the dust is being lifted."

It always amuses her to wind up where she intends to be without Google Maps or the old-school printed maps her father once spread across the dashboard. She has not dared to explore the cities since the pandemic escalated to stories of murder and thievery, but city grids gave birth to her internal compass and the loneliness of city life gave birth to these voices in her head.

As she looks out over the blooming sagebrush and brings attention to the noises of birds and soft wind around her, she remembers the conclusion of her young adult days living in Portland, Oregon, so close to nature, but so out of touch with Self. She chased man after man, those eager or not to be with her, always finding her Self left hopeless and lost, until she discovered how to break this disempowering cycle: navigating through it, rather than trying to get around it; pulling out the deepest roots from her many past lives and finding peace in letting them die.

Today is the full moon, the day of each month that brings high energy and the desire to socialize, like a coffee buzz. She is only a couple hours away by foot from the group of unfamiliar faces, but first, breakfast. She stares at the Sun, bare feet in the sand, feeling Her rays penetrate the body and fill it with warmth, the ground contributing to the Moon's energy stored within her. It is important she catches these rays in the morning, never sure what the weather will bring, or where a trading post may lead her.

It has been many moon cycles since her last trading post, where she offered her strength and endurance helping a woman carry a heavy load of goods in exchange for a small leather drum.

She moves her scarf from her neck and shoulders to shade her face, shakes off the rising sensations of lust and excitement with a bouncing movement, and follows her guidance down the mountain, peacefully aware.

Take notice to where you have wound up. What brought you here?

The Artist

Before she knows it, she is approaching the boulders, spray painted with illegible neon purple words by some vandals after the pandemic spiraled out of authority's control. She always finds beauty in this dead art form and wonders if any of the remainders have a new appreciation for graffiti, the modern petroglyph.

She can hear a faint drum pounding behind the boulders, and she sighs with relief—at least someone is here. Lifting herself up over the rocks, her bells jingle loudly, and the small group of people on the other side turn to face her. Smiles are rare these days, something that must be pulled out strategically like a cactus thorn in your foot, but she knows her capabilities and approaches the fellow nomads.

Although she studied many languages in her education and travels, words are used rarely, if at all, these days. Gestures explain everything, an abnormality normalized early into the pandemic to avoid opening your mouth and spreading germs.

There were about 20 people, some sitting in a large circle with their goods spread out across blankets while others shopped. In the few trade posts she has been to, she noticed there are three types of people at each trading post: vendors of necessities (food, water canisters, recycled sacks, etc.), vendors of collectibles (things scavenged from trash bins and deserted houses), and buyers.

Then there was her: the artist, the entertainer, the child who just wants to play. Because of her sun gazing and meditation rituals, she does not need to purchase the "necessities," so she wanders through the sprawling collections in case she wants to add something to her Magic Bag.

As she ponders over a woman's blanket of miscellaneous rubbish, she feels a penetrating stare and looks up with brutal confidence. It is important not to come off as too inviting with strangers, which her beauty does naturally. For defense, she has adopted a fierce look to ward off any misconceptions of weakness. But when she sees the young man staring at her with big, curious eyes, she notices her Self immediately shrinking back to the goods. "No double takes," she demands the body. Does she know him? Why does he look so familiar? Sparks of curiosity ignite, burning in the back of her eyes.

She continues at a turtle's pace, admiring the artifacts with each vendor and making as much eye contact as possible, until she reaches the man. Without looking at him, she focuses on his items for trade. A blank journal and pen catch her eye, a rare treasure—it must be worth more than she can give. She points at it looking up at him as if to ask how much, and he gives her a wide smile to which she is unaccustomed.

When he does not respond, she opens the Magic Bag and gestures for him to put his hand inside.

He does so without hesitation and pulls out a spherical rock about the size of a baseball. She just found it on her walk yesterday in the arroyo, smoothed over by the water centuries ago. She smiles shyly at him, is that worth a journal?

He looks at the rock, clueless, so she quickly grabs it from him and begins using it to massage her calf, then she tosses it back to him.

Taking a second look at the rock, then at her, he begins juggling it. The rock flies in circles in the air, rolling over his back, balancing on his nose, and shuffling between his feet. Her smile is uncontrollable, so she surrenders to it. She pulls five sticks out of the bag, about one foot each and holographic pink.

He stops juggling, amazed by the colors and curious about her juggling skills. To his surprise, she snaps the five pieces together: her most sacred treasure, a hula hoop.

She starts with it at her waist, moving it from waist to thigh, thigh to waist, up to the chest, shoulders and then neck. Halting the flow, she gestures for him to juggle once again.

Before they know it, they are the center of attention and everyone has deserted their things to circle around the entertainment. This is why she is here. The smiles, the laughter, the glowing eyes, letting go of everything tangible, she feels as if every happening in her life brought her to this very moment.

Life stops as she is spinning, and she loses her Self in the flow of the dance, like a meditation. The body separates from the mind and its judgment and hesitation, her spirit feels ecstatic—a rush of adrenaline—inspired by the excitement of the spirits surrounding her.

When the performance is over, everyone looks at each other with big smiles before returning to their stations. She turns to the young man, who has the journal and rock extended out to her.

She slides the book from beneath the rock, a gesture to let him know this toy is for him. He frowns at her and shakes his head side-to-side, glancing over at his collection on the ground. She understands he has too much to take with him already.

She catches a glimpse of sadness in his eyes, but one that has been there for many years, a glimpse of a plea for her to save him, to free him from the heaviness.

He hands her the rock and she turns to walk away holding onto the shared disappointment. She will continue to be the only artist, because no one values their creative abilities more than the load on their back.

Are you an artist, a creator? Or do you choose the load on your back?

Moving In

Smiling and nodding at everyone as she passes by, she exits the dwellings with a heavy heart and reminder of her loneliness. Even surrounded by people, she still finds her Self feeling isolated by her life choices, driven by curiosity rather than survival.

She never returns to where she came from, so she turns right after the rocks, moving west according to her inner compass.

It is about noon, so she finds a spot in the shade about a mile out of "town" to admire the new, but similar, desert landscapes from a new perspective. The bluish hues on the desert plants in the shade always cool her down, and she observes them closely for any signs of life to ground her back into the present.

An off-beat clinking sound rises from the east, and she looks back to see the young man running after her with a 60-liter bag on his back, metal cups and keys attached on the outside banging around.

He slows his pace when he realizes she has found stillness in the shade, and walks toward her with that big smile. She immediately sees through him, not around him: a boy dressed as a man, her inner child. As a mother understands the desires of a baby, a healer can sense the suffering of an inner child.

He kneels near her in the shade, letting the giant bag slip off his shoulders and land heavily on the ground, a sign he carries his weight on his shoulders, and a lot of it. He leans over, handing her the pen. "You might need this," he says with a smile.

The sudden verbal communication catches her off guard, until she realizes she has momentarily frozen staring at the pen. She grabs the pen with a quick scoop, as if to make up for lost time, and moves it to her bag.

"Is that all you have?" he asks, pointing at her small backpack.

She smiles with pride and says, "What more do I need if others carry it for me?" pointing at his bag. "Doesn't your body ache under the weight of everyone else's expectations?"

Stunned and slightly insulted, he begins to justify his actions, "Well I… uh… it's just that…"

"Keep it," she says interrupting him, "it's your weight, not mine."

Identify any weight which burdens you. Does it belong to you or someone else?

14

Guarded

When she walks, he follows, telling her a story about tripping, his bag smooshing his vertebrae against the ground. When she sits, he sits, waiting for her response. Does he want sympathy? She begins to get nervous with the night encroaching. First impressions never reveal the whole story of a person, and she surely does not know his. Where did all those things come from anyway? Is he a thief with that distracting smile?

"Dis-create," she thinks to her Self, the conscious spirit inside of her. Every thought is a prayer, and she knows the ways of manifestation, the power in creating reality from thoughts. She will have to remain positive if she wants a positive outcome.

She observes him as he looks out at the desert, his hair long, eyes big, tattoos down his arms and legs. He looks to be a few years older than she is, but the spirit he emanates feels so much younger. He wears ripped black shorts and an oversized green pocket T-shirt with holes. She cannot identify his ethnic roots or his accent.

A red flag raises at the uncertainty of his intentions in following her, and she feels panicked, the need to run, escape. She does not dart her eyes when he looks over at her, and she watches him survey her top to bottom, bottom to top. He speaks when he reaches her eyes again, "Tell me a story."

She glances over to the desert and lets the mind fall back to peace. A story… she suddenly misses the silence of being alone and smirks with her Self at her ignorant human tendency to crave what she does not have.

"Do you have a problem with silence?" she says with immediate regret. The truth is she wants to know his story too. "Why don't you tell me a story? The story that brought you to this very moment, you choose where it begins."

"But I asked you first!" he shouts playfully. It rings in her ears and she gestures to lower the volume. "Okay," he whispers, "How about I tell you how I know you?"

She freezes, regretting ever playing along with his silly mind games and, at the same time, returning to the burning curiosity. "How about you tell me why you're following me?"

"Because then I'd be telling the story backwards. Maybe it's because I like to read dumpster books and expired newspapers, but I still live in the box of left-to-right, top-to-bottom, and beginning-to-end."

She likes to play the game of mystery, answering questions with questions and speaking bluntly or with sarcasm, and she is excited to see he does too.

Have you ever craved what you didn't have? Have you ever regretted receiving something you asked for?

15

Past Bears Gifts

It is amazing how time suddenly exists with company. She only has a couple hours now until the sun sets, only a couple hours to get to know her potential camping buddy.

"I'll start by saying this: we have never met in this life, but throughout many of our lives. I don't know if you felt that connection during our performance."

She did recognize the synchronicity of their movements, as if they had danced together many times, but she does not permit her Self to admit that.

He continues, "I'm not sure how many people you speak with these days, but some of us are going through similar journeys of Self-discovery. I can tell you are wise and much older than me in spirit, like a mentor. There is a reason we come together again in each life."

She wants to laugh aloud and make him feel wrong, but she knows what he is saying. There was no random selection with the pandemic fatalities. There is a reason she survived, and the reason intertwines with everyone else's reason, but she cannot distinguish what her, or anyone else's, reason is just yet.

She has talked to many people over the years since the pandemic altered Life drastically, permanently, pondering this same question about why some survived while others did not. But without any concrete answers, she grew a love for silence and listening, careful not to absorb any ideas as Truth. Now, she never instigates conversation, she patiently waits for it.

"Now tell me why you're so insistent in following me," she demands, trapping her Self in the disappointing search for an answer, like some philosophical discussion about free will.

"You owe me something in exchange for that journal," he says nodding his head toward the Magic Bag.

She feels scared, unsure of what it is he is expecting from her. "So, what?"

"What I mean by that is you didn't pick up anything else or exchange energy with anyone else; you showed up today, the same day I did, chose my journal, and performed with me. You have a gift for me, but neither of us know exactly what it is yet," he concludes, casually looking off into the distance.

She keeps silent, reflecting on his unjustified beliefs, and scans the landscape around her for the perfect place to ground for the sunset.

"Atop that hill," the voice in her head guides her. She grabs the Magic Bag, bells jingling loudly, reinforcing awareness to the wandering mind.

Have you ever met someone who had a gift for you, or you a gift for them?

ne gift of

how blessed we are
to inherit the opportunity
to live over... + over...
+ over
again...

.ife

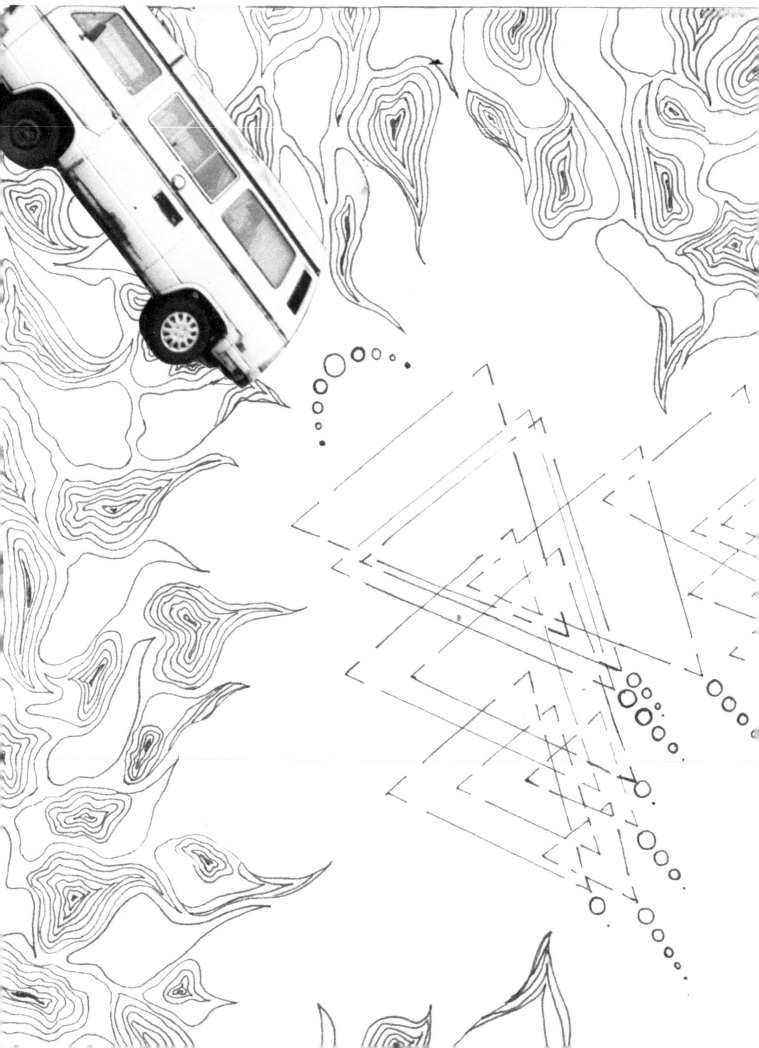

Gifted

Hiking up the small hill without explaining where or why, she finds a comfortable place to sit by the trees, crossing her legs and resting her palms in her lap.

She notices he does not follow, and she is pleased that he allows her this time for her Self. Things are going to be very different moving forward if she is going to have a companion, and she focuses on "positive" imagination, when she remembers that right or wrong, good or bad, positive or negative are all just illusions that color her perceived reality. She sits peacefully with the idea that what is meant to be will be.

This is the life she chooses to live, a life of flow and ease, not judging or expecting any specific outcome to her actions, or at least the life she strives to achieve.

She moves her attention to the Sun, absorbing Her remaining light into the body; she can use this energy very effectively, in fight or flight, if stored properly. As the sun sets, she notices the smell of burning sage. Peeking behind her over the hill, she can see the boy busy building a fire, plucking the bushes around him for an easy ignite.

Her curiosity still burns as she heads back down the hill in the dark to the campsite, and she desires to unravel the mysteries of who this boy is, what gift she has to offer, and why she carries it for him. She takes a seat next to the seeds of a flame just starting to grow. He sits down directly next to her and, without hesitation, the body moves her left hand up to his heart, her eyes close. She is searching for an image, something to understand his pain.

He takes an unsettling breath, his chest rising and falling beneath the palm of her hand. She opens one eye to squint at him, but he is looking down at the fire. His gaze travels over to her, "I can see now what you're here for, but I worry I am not ready to receive your gift, if it means letting down my barriers."

She slowly takes her hand off his chest and positions the body toward the fire. Silence has proven to be the guide of transformation, creating space for a person to reflect on their own words. It is unfortunate to her that most people assume the opposite, which is to talk it out immediately, to defend, to retaliate.

They remain silent for half an hour or so. He bridges the gap expanding between them by shifting to rest his head on her lap. This does not faze her; it is as if she always kept that space empty for him. She shakes her head, doubting her Self, wondering if she is falling for some sort of psychological trap. Is all this past-life-talk nonsense? She feels the urge to flee the situation before it turns for the worst. He pushes her bag out of the way, bells jingling.

Inhale. Exhale. Inhale awareness. Relax into this moment. It is she who carries the gift after all.

Consider the possibility that you too hold a gift, something which you give to others. How have you helped others in the past?

Solo

The moon rises and falls slowly, and she does not sleep even one minute. After last night's nightmare, running from a pack of wild men, she wants to stay conscious, to avoid manifesting any unwelcome realities with the boy next to her.

He stirs every now and then, always readjusting himself on her leg, but she continues meditating through the moon's transition.

She completely separates the Self from body and mind, observing herself from an outsider's perspective, a bird watching a young woman meditate. She sees the body sitting next to her, but not his spirit, the access point to the mind. How can she enter?

Her astral body walks in a slow circle around them, and kneels next to her physical body. "Leave," she says softly, "He's not ready for you."

Her eyes burst open, and she looks down at her lap. She sees all his childish features: love, curiosity, non-judgment, things you can only notice about a person when they sleep.

It pains her to abandon him, as she felt, from the moment they exchanged the rock, he is hurting badly from past traumas of abandonment and those open, neglected wounds. But she must listen to her Self. Whom will he turn to if she is not there next to him? She hears the voice in her head ask, "The answer is in the question, isn't it?" All she can discover is it will not be her.

She maneuvers her leg from beneath his head laying his head gently on the desert floor. Gathering her bag, the bells jingle loudly. He sits up startled, "Are you okay?"

Unsure what to do next, she blurts, "I am leaving."

Dazed and half-asleep, he gets up and stumbles toward her grabbing her arm. Panic rises and she feels a prickling sensation shoot down her spine. A stranger's voice comes out of her mouth, "Don't touch me." She can feel the deadly glare, like the sun's beams shooting from her eyes at him, and he quickly drops her arm, stunned and obviously hurt.

"I am sorry, I didn't mean to hurt you…," he whispers softly.

She immediately turns to walk away, tears filling her eyes. Her heart hurts recalling his words, his shame and blame, and she feels his pain as if it were her own. How can he blame himself for what she has done, is doing?

Without turning back, she exits into the night.

Make a list of all the things you abandoned. Can you forgive your Self?
Make a list of all that has abandoned you. Can you forgive them?

Journal Entry 1

Dear Moraine,

It is light outside finally, and I am alone at last, so I write to you.

I am tired of being apart in the company of others. Your thoughts are so much more pure than mine are; you are nicer, more virtuous.

I used to smile and laugh at everything just like you. Now I feel as though I am trapped in a body, where even the simplistic, beautiful function of smiling is prohibited.

When I go to speak, my mouth remains shut, locking me inside.

I have good intentions, obviously you know, but even my meditative practices—to open up the box of hidden memories, feelings, and ways of being, and reach inside—don't lead me to you. I still remember the backhanded compliments I received when I was drunk or high, "You're so nice! You're so fun! Why can't you be like this always?"

Where is the satisfaction hiding in the places I seek it out? Why don't I feel full? Is it not having someone to love, someone who understands? But how can we expect anyone to understand us if we do not understand our Self?

I am not a loner, are you? I long for relationships, whatever that entails. Am I not ready or are they not ready? Does my light fade as quickly as it draws people in?

Please, send me someone who can help me in return for my help.

What do you desire, but don't yet have? Do you know your Self as someone who is ready to receive this?

Goddess

She closes the journal and looks out over the rolling hills. Her favorite part about Life is how rapidly everything changes. Sometimes she worries she might like change too much, the free moving wind that blows through the stationed trees, sometimes destructive and other times reproductive.

Wondering what the boy might be up to, she quickly grabs her bag and sets out for walking meditation to sever his lingering presence from the mind.

A couple hours into her walk, parked in the shade of a small tree, sits a beautiful old native woman; a gray hair goddess, she thinks. The woman's strong cheekbones raise higher, almost completely covering her eyes, with a wide grin as she sees the girl approaching.

She is amazed to see another single female, not to mention a person who is smiling in her direction without her having to instigate it, but she returns the smile nonetheless, grateful for today's unusual gifts.

The old woman raises a frail arm to wave over the wanderer, revealing a small bag dangling from her neck, no other luggage around her, and the girl acts accordingly without hesitation, excited to connect with another weightless wanderer.

"You better be careful walking barefoot around here! I've already seen a few rattlesnakes burying themselves in the sand this morning."

The girl is not insulted by the lecture, but grateful for Life's warning signs. "Do you really believe we've made it all this way, through everything that's happened, just to be killed by a snake?" she asks genuinely interested in the woman's perspective.

"Of course I don't, but if you think your journey simply ends with a snake, then you are overlooking a deep Truth," the old woman responds.

She ponders this idea for a moment when the woman asks, "Do you know an omen?"

She was introduced to the idea of omens just a couple years before the pandemic began, but only the general concept. Before she can answer, the woman continues, "An omen is a natural happening carrying a message from the Gods, knowledge passed down from generations of ancient tribes. It is best, if you're going to wander these desolate lands, you become well aware of your surroundings and the messages from God."

It has been years since she received spiritual wisdom, her last mentor being a boss at the birthplace of her Awakening, the moment she became aware of her own consciousness.

She smiles and cocks her head curiously at the gray-haired goddess, taking a seat in the dirt within a polite distance as if saying, "Please, tell me more."

"I will tell you the omens of the snake, which depend on the context of one's current state of being: evil, transformation, or masculinity.

A snake is often seen as evil in many cultures; you must know Adam and Eve. If you receive a snake's bite in the context of evil, it is a karmic result of your evil doing to another. Perhaps you stole something or told a great lie. If you see a snake in the context of evil, it is foreshadowing a karmic event coming your way, such as being manipulated.

A snake can also represent transformation, like a snake shedding his skin. If he bites you, you are transcending beyond this plane, transforming into a new life. If you spot a snake in the context of transformation, it foreshadows new beginnings and various aspects of your life shedding away.

Lastly, a snake represents masculinity: competition, dominance or control, physicality, material, and aggression. If you are bit in this context, you may have become too powerful or aspired to have too much control. If you do not, it's foreshadowing a balance of masculine and feminine energies, a new appreciation for He who is in your life and in your Self."

The girl remains silent, patiently waiting for anything else, but the woman stares at her, creating space for a response. She stands, dusting the sand from her skirt, and thanks the old woman with a slight bow of the head.

"You are very knowledgeable; I appreciate your time today."

She wants to be alone now to meditate on the current context of her life, to reflect on this message.

The woman interrupts her departure, "Just so we're clear, snakes don't always come in reptilian form."

Confused as to whether or not a spell has just been placed on her, she nods her head again, letting the old woman know she has been heard, and continues on her way, carefully observing her surroundings for snakes.

What advice have you received recently? Given?
What message(s) can you receive when you disconnect the advice from the individual who gave it?

Context

She is perched on a hilltop, eyes closed avoiding the distracting flutters of nature. The word "God" still makes her feel unsure about a conversation, considering how "He" dictated every step of those who followed Him—or at least those seeking power used a skewed version of His message to demand obedience from their followers. She can remember the days when she would simply disregard a person for believing in something so big, yet so specific.

Now, she is trying to uncover for her Self the big, yet specific, mystery of why she, of all people, remain here on this Earth. Why did she not die with everyone else?

Since the pandemic and her heightened awareness to Life's messages, like snakes or the internal compass, she intuitively created her own concepts around the word "God", understanding for her Self that "God" was no different from "Universe" or "Life."

She sits meditating on the gray-haired goddess' wisdom and the current context of her life.

Is she evil for leaving the boy alone? Did she cheat him for the journal?

Or is this a transformative period? Is Life hinting at a new beginning as a healer or lover and shedding old layers of worry and doubt away?

She does not quite understand the idea of masculine versus feminine, and she is left with no answers. She laughs to her Self how ridiculous all of this is anyway, because if she dies from a snakebite, how can she even review the context?

She stares down at her feet, shoeless and worn. What a risk this life is. Every decision, every step is a risk that determines the next decision, next step. Risky, yet powerful.

Suddenly a scream echoes eerily through the hills, and she jumps to her feet. There is only one guess who it can be. She grabs for her bag when doubt voices to her, "What are *you* going to do? What if it's a man, or an animal, how will you protect yourself *and* save the woman? What if that witch is tricking you? She warned you not all snakes are reptilian!"

Her hesitation lasts only a moment before she recognizes the manipulative voice she once fell slave to. She has no idea where the scream came from, but the trusted voice in her head guides her through the trees, over the hill, back to the desert floor.

The heart pounds, arms pumping, until she kneels next to a paralyzed woman, the gray-haired goddess.

What is the riskiest next-step you can take? What's at risk?

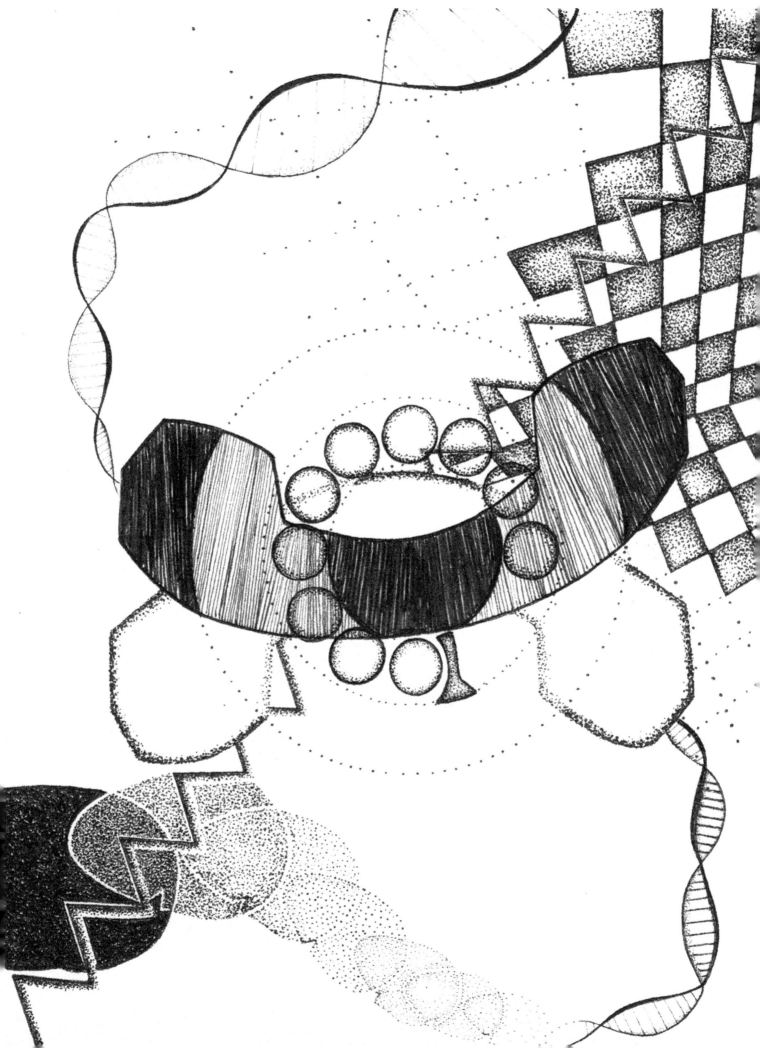

Deserted

She immediately grabs the woman's wrist for a pulse and, to her surprise, the woman jolts, her eyes flashing open.

"My foot, my foot…" she gasps, but struggles to reach through the paralysis. The girl glances down to her ankles, where a fresh snakebite pulses venom up through the woman's veins.

She has never had to save a life before, only witnessed a fatal motorcycle accident. A flashback of the body rolling past her car window and her feeling of helplessness waiting next to the unconscious body for someone, an angel, to approach.

Fear begins to creep over her, doubting her abilities to heal this woman. Although gifted, her lack of experience with snakebites limits her beliefs for success, and she momentarily forgets the power of thoughts and their manifested outcomes.

She throws the Magic Bag down, the bells jingle softly and she regains focus, smiling at the panicking woman. "Focus on your breath," she says calmly, perhaps trying to reassure her Self as she assesses the snakebite.

She attempts to encourage the woman to prop up to a sitting position, but the woman is losing consciousness and her body is swelling quickly. She tries to remove the rings from the woman's fingers to prevent circulation loss, but they are already stuck.

Beginning to panic, the mind goes blank, shutting down, and she remembers not to resist the intuitive work coming through her vessel. When the mind seems empty, it is only making space for Life to take over.

She sits behind the crown of the woman's head, hands hovering over both temples, eyes closed. A white light streams down through the crown of her head, passing through each crevasse of the body with a pulsing sensation. Her palms feel sweaty, tingly, but she does not take her focus off the white light projecting into the woman's temples.

The woman, with her eyes still closed, struggles to say, "I do… believe… I made… all way… to you… gift."

Each pulse gets less vibrant, less abundant, and she clings to it, begging it to stay with her. The grey-haired goddess is drifting now, turning from light brown to white to blue. She feels a change in the energy, a lightness, and notices that the woman's body has gone limp.

Her heart sinks into the ground and she sits frozen, in doubt of the perceived reality of the situation. A second body lies lifeless beneath her, and she feels defeated once again.

Make a list of all your "failures", then read the next story.

Magic Bag

She remains like a statue behind the woman's head for some time, completely absorbed by the thoughts running wildly in the mind. She feels numb, exhausted, unable to halt her ego from inflating like a balloon inside of her. Failure. Dumb. Incapable. This poor woman suffered because of her inability to heal. Life gave her a chance, but she failed.

Her eyes fall down on the corpse, and she notices a smile on the woman's face: simple, unlike her wide smile from earlier in the day, but content. At first, she questions if the goddess played some sort of trick on her–maybe she is a witch who knows how to play dead–but realizes immediately the misfortune that is the Truth.

It amazes her the rapidness a person can enter and exit life, how quick they come and go; how they can be there one second and then gone forever the next. She does not dare to ask the question, "Where to?" for she knows the answer will be revealed to her too one day, and until then it is only a waste of the present moment to project something so far beyond her human capacity to understand.

The smile somehow reveals waves of bliss, and she gets a sense that her work she thought "failed" might have actually helped this woman to a peaceful death. And what did she say amidst all the chaos? A gift?

She ponders over the riddle-like wisdom she received earlier of the omens, and fills with gratitude, what a gift. She has not quite uncovered the mystery of the context yet, but she knows the answers will come the moment she stops seeking.

She bows down, gently kissing the woman's forehead. A beautiful transformation.

As the body rises to its feet, she notices the woman's small medicine bag sitting a short distance away. It is just large enough for money or rocks, no food or water. Curiosity calls her over, and she tips the bag over revealing its contents: a round, spineless cactus.

She returns the items to the woman's sack, feeling like a thief at a murder scene.

But is this the gift she was talking about? The girl looks at the body once more confirming she is dead before blessing her with appreciation.

She digs into the Magic Bag, pulling out a mixture of wild tobacco, desert sage, and other herbs, and sprinkles them over the body. She lights a Palo Santo stick she has been savoring since pre-pandemic, and uses a round Asian fan made of colorful textiles similar to her bag to blow the smoke along the corpse. She takes the small sack with the cactus into her hands, slipping it into the Magic Bag.

She paces to the trees before sunset to ensure she spots any snakes.

Review your list of "failures" and ask, "How did this experience transform me?"

27

Journal Entry 2

Dear Moraine,

How unfortunate can fortune be?

When we have everything we want and need, a single loss is a huge misfortune.

How uncertain can certainty be? Or is the better question, how certain is uncertainty?

The greatest reward of all requires no effort but is simply handed to us. One moment we have it all, but any second we can lose it just as easy. And are we wrong then for fearing anything beyond our control?

What a waste, it seems, to never take a risk. The conditioned mind, which is all minds, goes one of three ways: left, right or straight. But what is this mind? It must be the opposite of what I want it to be and the same as what I am content with it as.

Where is room for context? It either is or it isn't, but either way it is what it is.

The variations of perspective alter the context, requiring one who wishes to see the Truth to remove the context entirely. I feel unfulfilled by this Truth, don't you? I'd like to believe through experienced proof that the context is more obvious and things are not so black and white.

What is our context here? What does the snake reveal to me? What is the context when you witness the agonizing death of another?

I am grateful for her gifts today.

Please, guide me to the answer, one in which I feel complete.

Define each direction of the mind… What does it mean for you to go right, left, or straight?

28

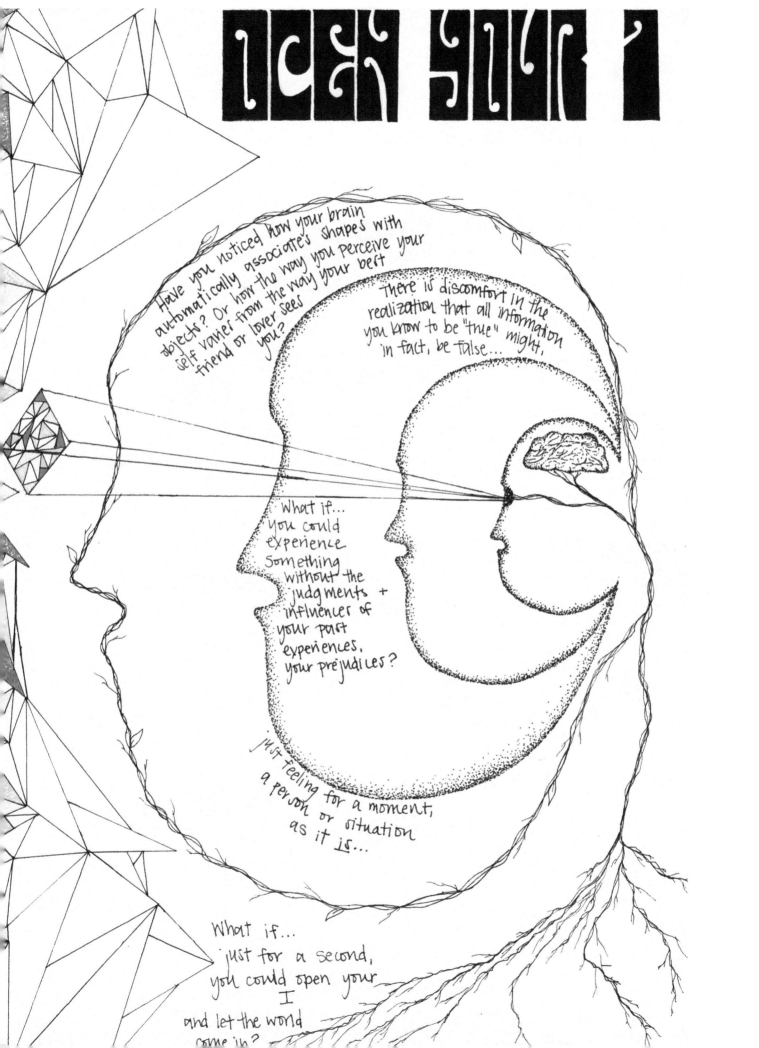

OPEN YOUR I

Have you noticed how your brain automatically associates shapes with objects? Or how the way you perceive your self varies from the way your best friend or lover sees you?

There is discomfort in the realization that all information you know to be "true" might, in fact, be false...

What if... you could experience something without the judgments + influences of your past experiences, your prejudices?

just feeling for a moment, a person or situation as it is...

What if... just for a second, you could open your I and let the world come in?

Snake

Dark approaches quickly, relieving her from the intensity of the day. The Moon greets her with a wide grin, despite being swallowed by the infinite black hole behind it.

She is exhausted, finding her space near the guardians of the desert. The grounded trees.

Her eyes close heavily, and she realizes she has not mourned the death of a stranger. The woman's last bit of knowledge fails to exist without her passing. She feels the pressure of gravity pulling down on her shoulders, the pressures of legacy eating away the muscle to carry its weight.

She feels nothing as far as tears and sadness, just an uncomfortable emptiness, as if all the energy she had absorbed from the sun since her first steps as a wanderer have flushed out of her. At least she tried to save the woman; at least she offered help when the mind told her not to.

With her eyes closed, she still feels and hears every creature around her. A wave is coming up over the hill toward her, and she opens her eyes. One by one, snakes are slithering up over the edge, moving toward where she sits.

She cannot move, can barely breathe, as the snakes sit heavily on top of her, wrapping their bodies tightly around each of her limbs.

At first, she is panicked. Snakes slither and coil on and around her, rattling and hissing at one another. But she finds the body and spirit are calm, like a mother nursing her baby.

It is not the snakes she is scared of, but the risk she takes by sitting with them. However, everything in this Life is uncertain; it could have been poisonous mushrooms appealing to her appetite.

It is life or death in every situation, but either way it is Life.

She finds comfort in the calmness of settling into what is, and sits patiently through the night, keeping intentional focus not to move or aggravate the snakes. She is mindful not to manifest an unwanted result.

The snakes rotate spots frequently for warmth, and each time, her awareness is brought back to the slowest rhythm of her breath possible, the most minute rise and fall of her stomach and chest. One even grips her leg, not yet penetrating the skin, but releases her slowly as it falls asleep.

Each time panic arises, she extinguishes it. "Whatever happens, happens." She will deal with the circumstances as they arise.

Reflect on the quote, "It is life or death in every situation, but either way it is Life."

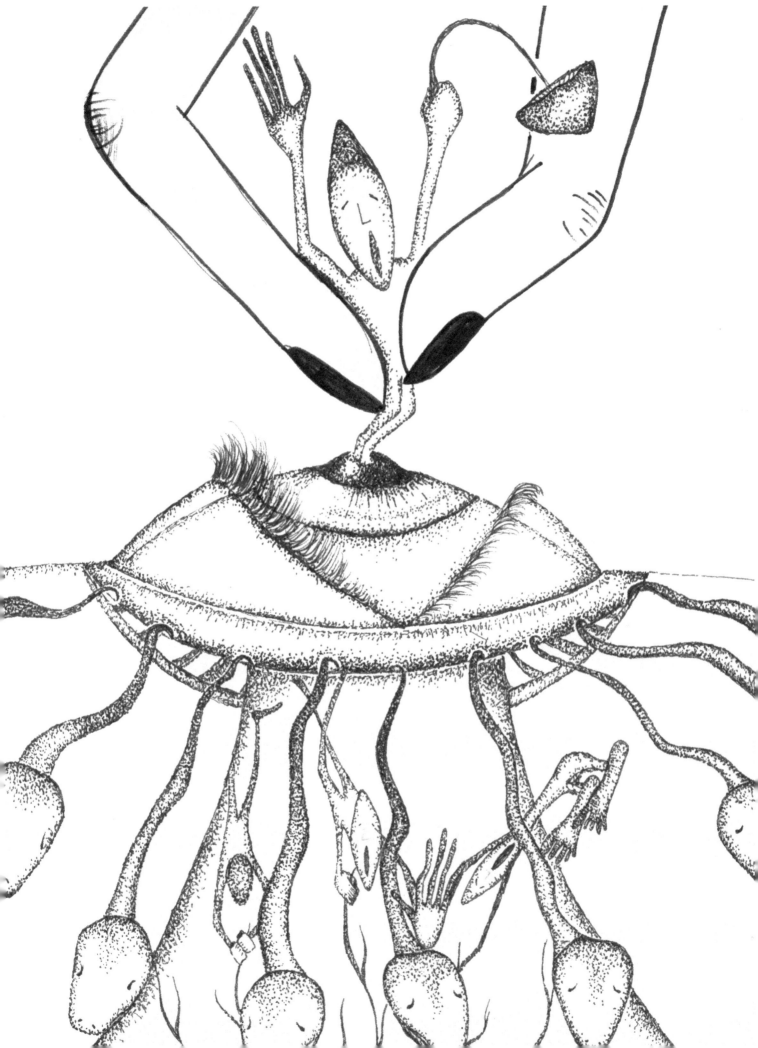

spirit

close your eyes.

notice how each breath travels down your spine and along every nerve, carrying life.

track the flow of your breath from the top of your head to the tips of your toes without letting a thought distract you.

notice how your mind wanders away from the body.

they are not one, but two, and your spirit is in observation of their dance.

Campfire

She lifts from the ground as the sunshine fills the darkness behind her eyelids. The snakes are gone and she smiles again at Life's jokes.

"What is all this snake symbolism?" she asks aloud to her Self. "Why now, all of a sudden?"

It has been months now wandering through the desert, and she was beginning to wonder if venomous snakes were always more rare than people were lead to believe.

Now suddenly she sees them everywhere, but never sees them at all.

Her senses bring awareness to a lingering smell of smoke in the distance, and she rises to her feet to look out over the desert floor. Forest fires do not bother the desert this far south, meaning it must be a campfire.

She grabs the Magic Bag and begins walking toward a thin trail of smoke down below, but she takes the ridge, the path least obvious to the campers, in case she gets a bad feeling and needs to escape unseen.

As she approaches, her memory races through the many camping trips sitting around a campfire. She was always so stoned, high on marijuana, so awkward with the strangers singing and telling camp stories around her. Although she felt so connected with nature in those trips, she felt something incompatible between her and the fellow humans.

She cringes at the memory of her always accepting the beer or liquor being passed around. The alcohol did not want to kill her, only she did. She begins erasing regret and filling the empty spaces of the mind with positive camping experiences, like when her friend excitedly pulled out a shaker to sing the only song he knew to her.

A young guy and girl sit enjoying breakfast on the desert floor. She checks for any negative sign of hostility or thievery, but only experiences calmness and the love of partners. Remembering her first trip to Asia, how intimidated her parents were on her behalf, a solo female in a foreign country. She felt insulted by their underestimation of her ability to sense danger, to plan her way around it spontaneously. It is just another risk.

The body carries her forward, her bells jingling as she picks up momentum down the hill, and she realizes it is likely more polite to introduce herself with grace.

The pair appears slightly panicked at a visitor's arrival, and she can see their bodies tensing, the exchange of uncertainty, as she approaches. Half not wanting to impose fear of threat on them and half enjoying getting any type of reaction out of these strangers, she approaches them with a smile.

What triggers your personal "smoke detector"?

City Dwellers

She continues smiling at the campers, her best smile, remembering to keep her distance and not to speak unless spoken to.

The guy waves, stepping in front of the girl as if to protect her. "Hello," he says, "Do you need some help?"

Humored by the offer, she smiles again and says, "No, I am just following the smell of campfire, so nostalgic."

"I'm sorry, are we not allowed to burn fire out here? We are coming from the cityscape, heading to where we think my girlfriend's family is living."

She looks around as if looking for someone to tell them they cannot have a fire, like the dangers are too high in sage brush, then responds, "I'm not here to stop you."

The girlfriend whispers to the boyfriend, not realizing that she can hear everything within a mile, "I think she is safe, let's invite her to sit."

She pretends she cannot hear the whispers and waits for the invite. The boy motions her over with a wave, picking up and dropping another heavy rock around the fire as a chair.

The girlfriend speaks with a strong southern accent, "The cities are still empty, deserted. We stay there mainly for resources, but even those have run dry, so now we are seeking help."

"I can't imagine the sight," she says with sincere compassion. Staring into their eyes, she feels their repressed pain, their desperation. Visions of the once bustling construction pop into her head, now a motionless destruction.

"Are you heading somewhere nearby? It doesn't look like you carry much with you," the boyfriend remarks, pointing at the Magic Bag.

"I am always connected to my necessities," she replies, explaining to them her holistic approach to living, how she survives without food, water, and humans. "My days out here consist of meditation… in all Her forms."

The couple glances at each other quickly, mouths gaping open, and then back at her.

Her assumption they are amazed by her commitment makes her ego inflate until the boy says, "We've been hearing so much about meditation in the last couple weeks! Even when we were digging through the dump on our way out we found a book on it."

The girlfriend gives him an I-told-you-so look, "The old woman did tell us the Universe keeps repeating things when it's trying to tell us something…"

Pretending not to hear his girlfriend's comment, he turns back to the girl, "So, how do you meditate?"

"Well," she pauses, still reflecting on what the girlfriend said about the old woman, "it would be easier to explain what it is not…"

Their stares are attentive, intrigued, so she puts the thought about Life's repetitions into her mental pocket for later and asks, "How would you define meditation?"

The girlfriend speaks up immediately, "Isn't it clearing your mind of all thoughts?"

"Now that sounds pretty complicated," she replies. She catches the girlfriend gazing upwards pondering the question deeper. "So that is how I would explain what it is not. What it is, is the flow between thought and awareness. Each time my mind wanders, I bring it back, knowing that eventually it will wander again."

She pauses for a moment then adds, "There is no end goal, such as clearing your mind, and it is not always sitting with your eyes closed as depicted."

"Ah," the couple says in agreement and the girlfriend asks, "Can you teach us?"

She shrugs her shoulders as if to say "why not?" From the Magic Bag she takes out a stack of gold metal chimes that hook onto one another, a gift from what once was Myanmar. When they clink against one another, they produce a relaxing vibration that hits certain points along the body, like a wind chime.

She crosses her legs and straightens her posture as the chime fades out. The couple awkwardly slides off their rocks and does the same.

"Begin by closing your eyes and focusing on the natural cycle of your breath, without trying to control it."

She peeks through a squinted eye and is pleased by their eagerness to learn. She finds the mind drifting back to what the girl had said about the Universe's signs, repetitive and cyclic, just like the natural breath.

As she guides them to a world of peace and tranquility, she feels a sense of fulfillment, the same way she feels when she is entertaining, when people are smiling all around her. She feels relieved of her failure to save the gray-haired goddess, knowing she can pass on the gift of Life another way. She feels peaceful, tranquil.

When she notices the mind wandering to yesterday's occurrences, she says aloud, "Congratulations if you find your mind is wandering. You are returning to the breath, you are reconnected with awareness, you are meditating."

Set a timer for one minute and meditate. Write about your experience.
How does it feel to notice the mind has a mind of it's own?

Key to Context

It is as if the couple transforms in one sitting. None of them knew how long they sat meditating, as if time matters. The quiet, the stillness, the warm morning sun, everything seems to support them on their journey to Self.

When they open their eyes, the colors are different, more vibrant, their bodies feel lighter; they have a sense of calmness they did not feel upon waking this morning.

"This has been the best introduction to meditation," the girlfriend says quietly, calmly, "and it is so amazing you just happened to wander by."

The girl smiles gently, receiving the appraisal with a bow of the head. "The Universe has been introducing you to meditation at the perfect pace for you, and I think it is a beautiful love story that you both are reaching this point of your journey at the same time."

The partners smile at each other, blushing. "What about you, what is your love story?" the boy asks with a friendly smile.

"I am still reading," she laughs, rising to her feet.

They invite her to stay longer and chat, offering her food before remembering what she had told them about her lifestyle. Feeling saddened by, or envious of, their romance, she decides she would rather be alone. She thanks them for letting her join their morning meditation, and they bless her on her walk with the gift of glowing smiles.

As she moves along on her journey, she begins to think about the context of her life through repeating patterns and cycles. Recently there has been a pattern of snakes, but she still cannot understand what it all means for the context of her life. There must be some deeper meaning, connected cycles, and she is not putting the puzzle pieces together yet.

The boyfriend's voice replays in her head, "What is your love story?" and her memory takes her back to the boy, who once lay his head on her lap. She knows where this train is going and she jumps off before the mind travels too far back in time. Not all love stories have a happy ending.

She wonders why some partners can stay together long term, forever, while others cannot. Her parents were happily married until she lost connection with them, and she assumes, with such a Life crisis as the pandemic, they were more than likely bonded together for security.

What would a psychologist have to say about her ongoing separations from lovers, sometimes her decision, sometimes her heartbreak, when the ideal American love story raised her, just slightly twisted roles of mom working, while dad stayed home?

Do you notice any themes in your life currently? What might the message be from this pattern?

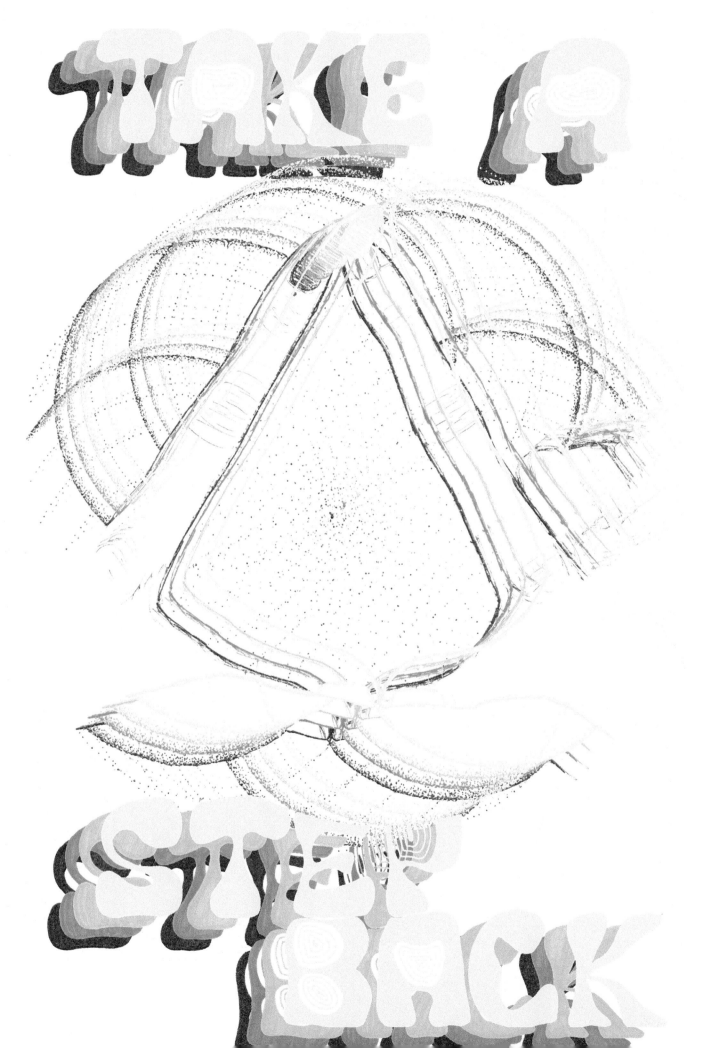

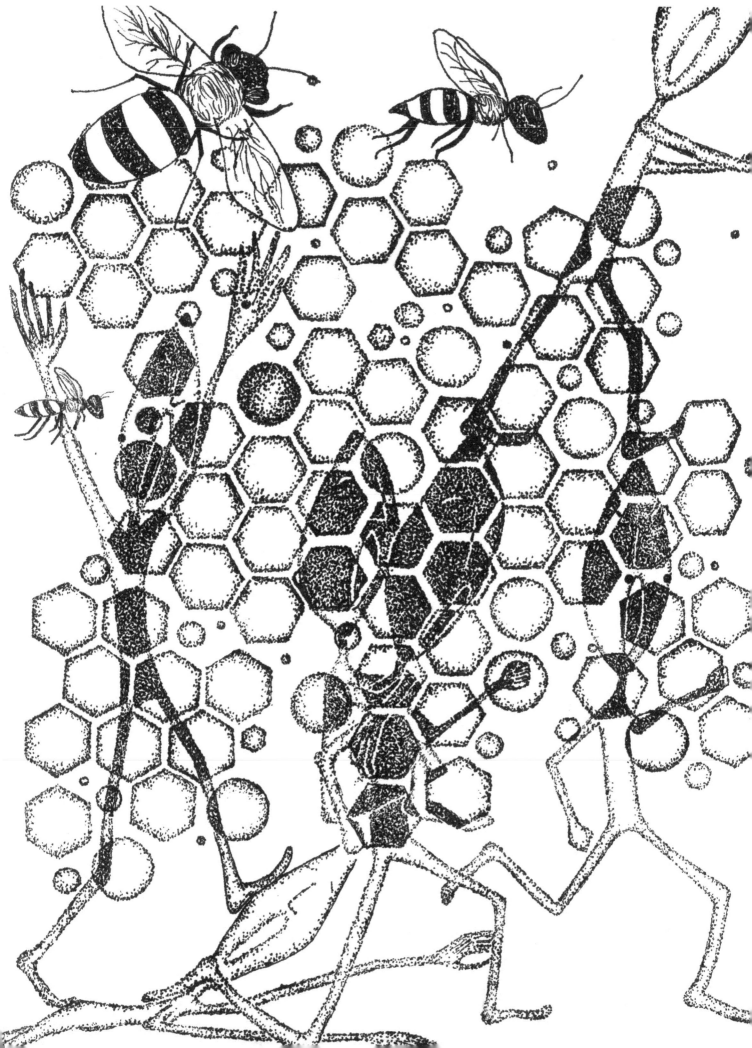

Destruction

All day she wanders without listening to her inner compass, all day she struggles to keep awareness, floating from reality into creeping memories from the past—stories of old lovers and friends. Each time she catches the mind wandering, she yanks it back with intense determination to think about anything else, eventually drifting again.

Her first lover scared her to the point of submission. Her second lover depended on her to the point of his own submission. Her third lover cheated her. One day she decided "no more lovers," fooling around with the illusion that is love. Boys turned to men who could only commit to their ideas of success, men turned to boys who could only commit to the physical touch, the wandering soul.

The same soul lingers from body to body, showing up in the perfect form for her each time and, at the same time, the worst form. It wished for nurturance, she wished for the same.

She moved locations frequently in search of answers to her prayers—a place that felt like home, a family, security, a companionship—always clinging to the body who seemed to fill this empty void at first glimpse. Soon enough, there were so many traumatic experiences that she just had to write off all her desires: the men, the women, friends, lovers, and intimacy in any form became prohibited. Is prohibited.

The worst part is, she knows it. She is completely aware of the darkness awaiting her if she ever braves the closed door. She has peeked a few times, seeing a vast space much bigger than she can manage, more desolate than the desert she wanders, and the heavy weight of a million deaths.

Today her hand holds the knob. The body rotates the knob right with a hand, the mind rotates it left, while her soul sits backseat in her own car. Her head swivels side to side with each rotation, until she feels the emergence of vomit. "Stop the car!" she demands.

Coming back to awareness, nearly choking for air, she falls to the desert floor, where she feels balanced, her bells jingling. What will it take to simply step inside?

She lifts her gaze up from the desert sand, her head and neck following. Down below she sees a snake-like pattern winding through the valley. A road. It is the first time she is realizing how long it has been since she crossed or even saw a road, a footpath to the cityscape.

The winding of the road, the turning of her head, snakes slithering, everything creating a psychedelic mess of the mind. How can she find clarity in a world of so many decisions, so many hurts, so many changing paths and directions?

Determined to find clarity, she picks herself off the floor and makes her way down the hill, never taking her eyes off the man-made mess of nature.

What can you assume is hiding behind your closed door?

In Route

As she approaches the cement, she is empowered by Mother Nature's ability to take back what rightfully belongs to her. Cement, something so indestructible by hand, is shattered by a sprouting leaf or a root.

She drops to her knees again, this time in awe of the beauty in destruction. The cement crumbles into small bits that will continue to break down over time, nearly disintegrating into air.

Life jokes with her, and she becomes aware of the fact that concrete, although man made in its form, is no different from the smoothed rock she discovered in the ancient riverbeds: just a rock made up of many rocks. No different from the next rock. Yet, here she is, condoning man for "hurting" something much greater, much wiser than the Self.

Does Mother Earth have to "take back" what is already hers? Perhaps the road is not being destroyed by the plants growing on and around it, but simply self-destructing as rocks do, allowing the plants to grow again.

She begins to see visions of her own cells, how a small cut on her knee will heal over again.

In this moment, this Truth, she feels so connected to her Mother. "You have shown me that I also have the ability to take back," she whispers to her Self before laughing uncontrollably with Life. She wants to scream for being caught up in the delusion of having no say in her reality once again, but it is not her preference to shout, for she hates to disturb the quiet peace. However, the quiet is strong, just like Mother, just like her. It will drown out the noise once again.

She bends over until her forehead rests on the Earth and she breathes slowly, grounding and connecting deeper. There is much to understand in the illusion she has been living, and it is going to require her to come face to face with the Truth, however brutally honest it might be.

What she once viewed as the destruction of her past, her intimacy, her ability to relate and connect with other beings, suddenly fits into a cut on her skin as she watches it all heal over. She understands what is possible, the power and healing she holds deep within her.

This longing for connection has been a call to return to her own disconnect, that of the mind, body, and Self. When, with who, and why? She opts to sit in the backseat this time, "Please, take me for a ride."

What wounds remain open for you? Do you possess the power to allow it to heal?

EVERYTHING COMES TOGETHER, ALL YOUR QUESTIONS GET ANSWERED, EVERYTHING YOU NEED IS RIGHT IN FRONT OF YOU, AND SUDDENLY YOU ARE IN TOTAL CONTROL OF THE REALITY YOU EXPERIENCE. IT'S AS IF YOU FIND YOURSELF IN A DIMINSION OUTSIDE OF THE THIRD, AND ALL PARALLEL UNIVERSES RIDE SIDE BY SIDE, ALLOWING YOU TO STEP OUT OF THIS EXPERIENCE † INTO ONE THAT IS BETTER SUITED TO YOUR PREFERENCES.

bloom

Past Life

As she turns the doorknob to the right, a cold draft brushes her skin and goosebumps rise. She always wondered if this prickling skin is a defense mechanism of the body. If so, why? If not, what?

The darkness swallows her before she has the chance to slam the door shut, and she surrenders to what is so. Without the urge to resist, to fight, she floats lightly through nothingness.

It is almost like one of those Disneyland rides, when she sat in a chair bolted to the ground, the lights around her dimming like a movie theatre. Suddenly, horrific skeletons and ghosts are projected around her, next to her, directly in front of her. The chair moves frantically back and forth, as if she is going through an underground tunnel on a train.

The skeletons are so lively, and the longer she sits with them, the calmer she becomes, the more entertaining they become. This one looks her dead in the eyes, and she gasps, seeing that it is she, her at 12-years-old. She cannot stand to see it, she turns right, it is 17-year-old her. She looks around frantically, shocked by the skeleton of every phase of her life, her past lives.

When she closes her eyes for safety, the inside of her eyelids become a screen projector, and memories display themselves in front of her, as if her eyelids are sewn back so as never to close.

Waves of memories come and go, some really humorous, beautiful and others very painful to watch. Traumas playing out entirely show her that she is so hooked on one tiny fragment of its entirety; these traumas became illusions and these illusions became her Truth.

A man leans over her limp body, she cannot speak or move. His eyes are filled with sorrow, but sorrow which he is unaware of, in denial of; the eyes of hopeless destruction. Through his lens, clouded by illusion, he cannot see how he is hurting her when he takes advantage of her paralysis. Because he refuses to open his eyes, he is unable to see beyond his own pain.

The man's face flashes to a handful of familiar faces—her parents, siblings, teachers, lovers, friends, and even parents of friends—all with the same eyes, all with the same hurt. A chill runs up her spine as she watches the projection of these familiar faces, having thought she would never see them again, some of them permanently erased from her memory.

Tears immediately begin rolling down her cheeks. When she looks closer, all she can see in their eyes is the reflection of her Self.

Consider each distinct phase of your life a past life...
Can you separate the stories, the illusions, from the facts?

Healing

She slowly raises her forehead off the ground, her back muscles tensing as they pull her weak body upright. Her cheeks are tear stained. Her heart pounds softer, returning to an even flow as she takes in the space around her.

Looking at this road for what it I, an extension of nature–rather than what she always thought it to be, destruction of nature–she feels deeply connected to Mother Nature.

She lowers herself on her side and rolls to her back to look up at the clear blue sky. She sees her Self in the sun's rays, the sky's hues. At first glance, the sky is blue, and the longer she stares into it, the farther the color wheel rolls, revealing white, purple, yellow, and green. When she turns her head to look at the vertical mountains, she sees her Self in the peaks, in the fractures, and in the plants that root into it, how they are all held together as one but separated by the mind.

She closes her eyes and sees her Self in the goddess, the same smile, a shared wisdom. She sees her Self in the boy, his pain in abandonment and his longing for love. It is a double-edged sword, reflection, because it is not unique to only the good traits.

Opening her eyes, she wipes the dry salt from her face. She wonders if crying is also a defense mechanism. The body, although weak, feels lighter, for the first time noticing the weight she was carrying. She knows she cannot hold a grudge on what is so and yet expect anything to change or develop—a home, family, love.

These pains, these destructions, grasping into the void, were never anyone's fault but her own. Is she even at fault? What is so is what is so, and the mind creates meaning around it. Like anything in nature, whatever she creates will eventually return to its natural state.

She gathers some strength to laugh softly with her Self. If there is no one to blame, then there is no one to forgive; instead of awaiting an apology, she is able to let it all go now.

Now she understands why the goddess died smiling. It is the feeling of freedom, of lightness and ease, of letting go. She suddenly cannot wait to die, but is quickly reminded of her past lives, how many times she has already died, experiencing more and more content with each rebirth.

As the Sun begins Her descent behind the mountains and the colors spill out over the Earth, she sits up, gently pulling the journal and pen from her bag. To her surprise, the gray-haired goddess' sack falls out. She opens it again, but just enough for one eye to peek through. The cactus looks back at her, and she wonders what this gift brings.

She returns the sack to its place in the Magic Bag and opens her journal. Words are coming to her faster than she can write, and she feels her cells healing over again.

Make a list of all the wrong-doings done to you.
What is it costing you to hold onto the fear, hate, guilt, etc.?

Journal Entry 3

Dear Moraine,

Today I must have aged many years, because I lived many lifetimes.

I saw my Self, and I saw my Self in all of them—those who came in and out of my life faster than the moments we shared. It is as if I have just unlocked the door to all my memories, but almost like I intentionally hid the key from my Self until this point.

Now I see me in you, and you in me. There is no longer this sense of separation, no need for unconscious isolation. Everything is not what it seemed, and I just wonder to what extent is this true.

I want to see, like I have just now, and understand the depth to which I lived in this illusion.

The road is not always great,

but I am grateful for the road.

This road, my journey,

brings me to awareness, to Truth.

For this awareness I am blessed.

For this blessing I am grateful.

I am aware that these mountains move me

and I have the ability to move these mountains.

What events in your life are you willing to take a second look at?
Are you willing to accept an event is not as it seemed?

Truth

She walks slowly along the road, thinking back to a film she watched in high school: hovering cars connected to the road through some magnetic system. The visions of the future were driven back in time with the pandemic. She does not know why she has chosen to follow the pavement, but she trusts that it will take her directly where she needs to go.

Today she decides to allow her imagination to run wild. She takes her place in the back seat, and surrenders to the reality of what is. She intends to start at day one, with the first humans she ever met: her parents.

At some point during the chaos of the pandemic—when all methods of communication shut down, not too long after money lost its authority—she lost contact with her family. Detachment and independence appeared to be genetic in their blood, and each member followed their hearts home. But home is not a single place to be with family anymore, home is where you find your Self; and it just so happened, each member found themselves headed in different directions.

For so long, she questioned the definition of "family" and "home," hopping from city to city, friend group to friend group, partner to partner, until today, she found her answer: Illusion, all of it.

Her childhood house is large, spacious. Everyone has their personal space, separated by walls and a lock, all on the same floor. Her room is a light, earthy green with a dark brown wooden office desk, vanity, bed, and armoire. Her windowsill is lined with a bright yellow cushion, covered with sunshine and floral pillows. The flower child. She wonders what is Truth— destiny or cause and effect? Did her childhood design make her this way, or was this way of being determined before she entered the world, therefore always shaping her reality to bring her to the now?

She sits atop the yellow cushion, legs crossed and eyes closed. Every door is open and the house is empty, everyone moving in their own direction. Her spirit detaches from the mind and body, and she begins to examine each room, assesses the person living in it, the qualities that drove her crazy and the ones that inspired her, and the archetype of each quality in her Self.

For the first time ever, she can see everyone, family or not, for who they actually are, rather than who she always projected them to be. Beyond that, she can see who she actually is without the projections of others.

A lifetime is flashing before her, revealing to her in many glimpses the reality that is Life, the interconnectedness of all beings rooted at the same source, driven by the same things—home, family, love. The mind establishes itself in a newly discovered compassion for everyone, no different from her, and she is inspired to look deeper through a new lens.

What archetypes make up your family?
How do these archetypes make up you?

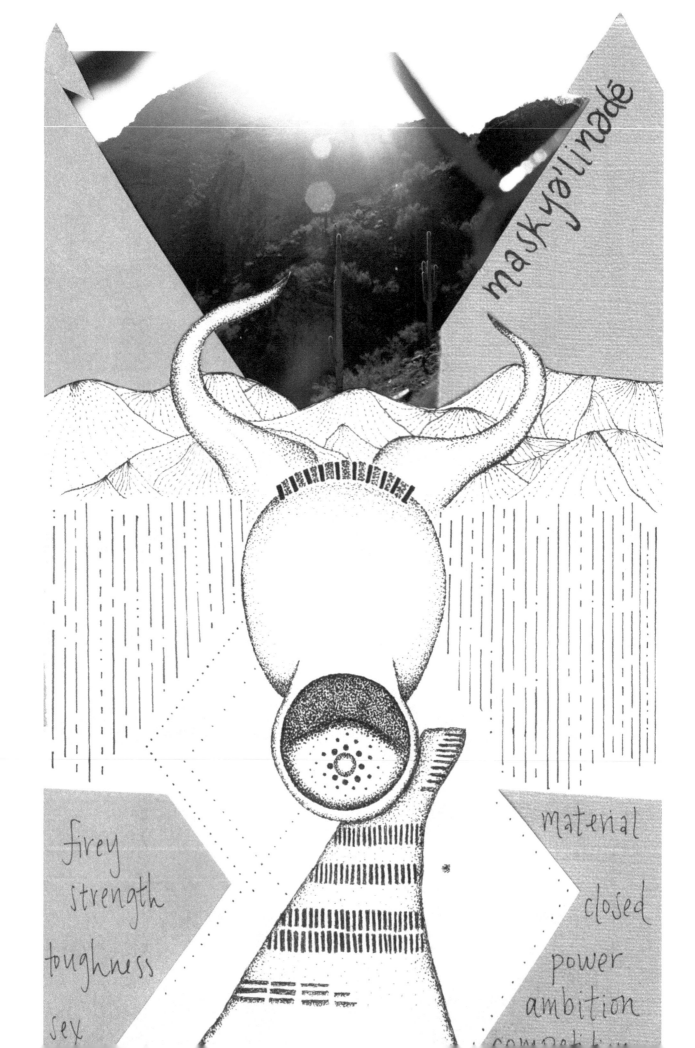

mask/ə'linədē

firey
strength
toughness
sex

material
closed
power
ambition

Masculine

She staggers drunkenly with a group of unfamiliar faces toward the music. Her invite came from a nameless man. What does a name matter when a smile is so big and welcoming?

She was floating from person to person, group to group, when this stranger picked her up running straight into the ocean—fully clothed. Her makeup runs, curls falling heavy with water, but she is not scared nor startled at the fact she is alone with a strange man in the dark ocean.

His arms are strong and she feels safe. His smile is so big, she feels loved. What a man, blonde hair and blue eyes. His ease and confidence carry her through the night; she feels like she is floating through space with him, where other faces are just stars and he is the Sun.

It is as if this nameless man is as speechless as she is, and they communicate with laughter and smiles, not words, absorbed in the illusion of now. Life flashes forward and they are walking, clothes and hair air-drying, amongst a group of unfamiliar friends—his single male friends.

She is still floating on the cloud, when a heaviness sits in behind her. It feels like a dull dagger piercing her back—soft, but threatening.

Naive and drunk, she turns back to see a man, her father, walking swiftly to follow her. His eyes are hidden behind his heavy eyebrows. Red cheeks frame a stressed mouth, the corners falling to gravity, just barely skimming the ground. She immediately understands she has done something *very* wrong. She stops dead and the group of boys keeps moving, the boy not even realizing she has disappeared.

"Where is your sister?" he says harshly.

"I will find her," she blurts, ducking her head and pushing into the crowd. She feels naked, embarrassed, desperate for any feeling of safety, missing the boy's loving smile and strong arms.

Experience through recall is different, knowing her dad must feel the same way, too: scared and longing for safety. What father could live with the possibilities of his daughter snatched out of his sight in a foreign world? Somehow, they took the same steps toward safety on their individual paths. The same roots growing different flowers.

She does not have to live in shame or anxiety this time around, when she is not living an illusion, the illusion that her father may have been disappointed in her, or that she ruined the family holiday. Love is portrayed in many ways, some make her feel safe, others make her feel attacked, both make her recoil.

Identify the two types of masculinity in your life: shadow & light.
Describe a character in your life for each type.

49

Feminine

She is barely old enough to be aware of her Self. Her mother is her best friend, her soul mate at these times.

A loving warm embrace is all she needs from her mother to feel complete, to be a part of this Life. She is at that age when nothing else seems to matter, much like a baby monkey who pays no attention to the world around it, but grabs onto mom's dangling earlobes and pulls her long hair.

Of course, the mother is also filled with a prideful love, my baby. She cannot help but kiss the baby's swollen, soft cheeks and find amusement in the child's curiosity. Mother feels like an artist, the creator of Life and time, and she leans over to kiss the baby again and again, all over her face.

She grabs mom's face with excitement and pulls their lips together, holding the connection a few seconds too long.

Mother gasps, her eyes changing expression. She grabs the girl's tiny hands and she says sternly, "Mommy and baby never hold their kiss on the lips."

Embarrassed and confused, she is torn inside. Has she done something wrong? Is mother angry?

Nothing else is said, but mother moves away from the child and suddenly the bond, the moment of love and unity, is shattered.

Only a couple years later, mother will take off on a two-week work trip to a foreign world. The child sits quietly crying on the staircase, hiding in a place she knows she can easily be found. Mother overhears her crying eventually and comes around the corner.

She cannot remember the words exchanged, just mother's irritation at her for crying and the fact mother leaves anyway. Is it her fault? Is she not worthy of mother's love? If not a mother's love, then whose? Are her tears not reason enough to make someone stay?

She laughs now at the memory, how she has lived through the lens of "I am not worthy of love" all these years, unconsciously self-sabotaging her relationships in every past life.

As an adult, she put her mother through those same tears, a result of her adopted defense mechanism, "Fine, leave then, I don't need you!" She can see her Self in her mother's eyes, a feeling of not being enough is all they had in common, but not something they could share.

She shouts, "I love you!" at her mom, and when she does she can see the echo fade through the caves of her mother's pupils, landing with a splash in her own reflection.

Describe a mother's love.
How does it differ from Self-love?

'femanan

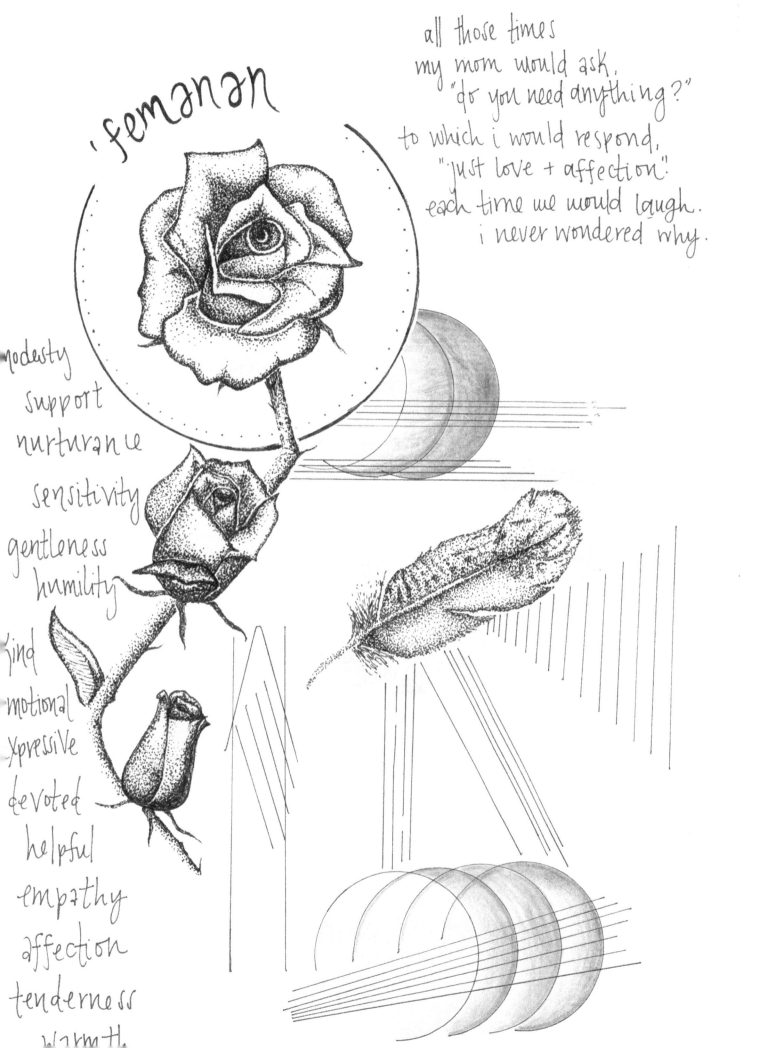

all those times
my mom would ask,
"do you need anything?"
to which i would respond,
"just love + affection"
each time we would laugh.
i never wondered why.

modesty
support
nurturance
sensitivity
gentleness
humility
kind
emotional
expressive
devoted
helpful
empathy
affection
tenderness
warmth

Cityscape

She is climbing a long mountain pass, following the now straight road for the time being. Her heart is pounding as she breathes deeply, but her endurance is youthful, her energy high. Her bells jingle and she remembers the comfort that comes with pulling her attention away from the mind and just admiring the beauty of physical existence.

The mountains are a gradient from deep red to snow white. When the light reflects off the white, it is almost too bright for her to look and she finds protection looking int0 the dark green trees and shrubs growing in every direction out of the cliffs. Massive boulders balance effortlessly on the slopes and she wonders when they will crash onto the road, which is already littered with shattered rocks.

It amazes her how naïve she can become, how unaware of her surroundings she is, when she strays too far back in time. So many things go unseen when looking backwards.

Reflecting on human's concept of time always makes her giddy, mainly because she is no longer trapped in the confinements of deadlines, birthdays, and other timely obligations and expectations. How easy Life is without the non-tangible structures created to condition her and everyone else. "Ensuring cooperation and proper protection," the "authority" might have said. She wonders if they actually meant it or if there was a larger agenda underlying it all.

Finally nearing the top of the road, she eagerly anticipates what lies beyond the ridge. She envisions a forest, but knows right away that must not be it. She has learned a thing or two regarding creation on her journey and is aware that Life does not usually give you what you think you want, but rather what you need. She wants a forest, but needs an interaction webbed with signs to point her in the next direction in Life.

The body halts at what opens up in front of her: a city. She feels silly for not expecting this after all Life's forewarnings: the city dwellers and talking about not having been to a city since the pandemic, but most importantly her desire to connect… her own manifestation. Rolling her eyes at Life with a quick laugh, as if a ridiculous joke has just been told, she moves forward with an unexpected eagerness.

She is brave. She is wise. She does not dare turn back. She trusts that Life always presents to her what she needs. What spreads out below the mountains is vast and widespread; what used to house millions of people is now a nearly desolate array of empty homes.

Mansions perch high in the mountains, while apartment and townhomes cower below. Human conditioning, again, becomes present, and she feels a deep sadness for the people who repressed their spirit, their creativity and curiosity, for the sake of living on the top of a mountain. Now, she wanders these hills, detached from any concept of wealth, rich with creation.

Make a list of everything you want.
How might life present this in exactly the way you need, but not the way you expect?

Part 2

Crystal

She floats quietly through the outskirts of the city. The impoverished houses look as she imagined them—were she to let the mind wander during her time with the desert. Doors hang off their hinges, windows shattered; trash blows around, stuck in every crevice; spray paintings of names she cannot make sense of decorate broken down train cars and useless automobiles.

It is eerie, the only noises consisting of the wind blowing and rats scurrying. As she walks through the narrow alleyways between warehouse foundations, she feels as though she is an alien on a planet far from home. She is alone in the loneliest sense of the word.

She walks slowly, listening for sounds nearing her space, but so far nothing. Passing through a trailer park, curiosity calls her to peek in the broken windows. Empty liquor bottles scatter the floor; an ashtray sits piled high with butts. She feels a ping of sadness for the person who lived here before, lost in the illusions of craving and uncertainty. Shaking her head, she is reminded of her own reflection in each situation. She also craves–the only difference being what for.

It is not until she reaches an intersection of highways that she understands where she has landed: Phoenix, Arizona, or what once was. She traveled this highway on a road trip to California, stopping to experience some local street art and "authentic" Mexican tacos on a Tuesday.

She follows the highway to the same exit she remembers taking on that day, entering the skyscraper district. The doors are all ajar. The landscaping has all overgrown, and she wishes cities had always welcomed the wild like this.

The buildings rise and she feels so small wandering through the concrete structures, so symbolic of how they might make a resident feel before the pandemic: small, unnoticed. Even the most outspoken person may become mute or feel transparent in such a place.

A door nearby swings open, and she jumps behind some bushes. A girl of about twenty-five appears, arms piled high with supplies left behind by corporate workers. From the bush, she can make out ground coffee, a mug, and some papers. If it were not for her attire, she would have guessed the girl was a secretary starting on her boss' daily errands.

The girl wears baggy black pants, a red tank top with no bra, and simple white shoes. Her dark hair curls naturally and she looks side to side anxiously for any passersby, then turns back to the door, gesturing for someone to come out.

56

Three guys follow her out, each with heavy pockets and loaded arms. They walk quickly toward the alley, the girl frequently checking behind her.

She stays hidden in the bushes, unsure of what they might do to a witness. When they turn the corner, adrenaline lifts the body up and she immediately sets out after the group, hiding amongst the shadows of the overhangs. When she reaches the street where they turned, she stops suddenly, thinking to her Self, "What's my intention in following these thieves?" She hesitates for a moment and then remembers it is not what she wants, but what she needs.

When she turns the corner, her face nearly smashes into another's. The girl. At first, her face is expressionless, obviously waiting.

"Can I help you?" the girl asks coldly.

She is speechless, confused by the tricks at play here. "I'm sorry," she says casually in an attempt to hide her weakness—fear, "I'm coming in from the desert... just curious what the cities have turned into."

The girl smirks, "You're lucky you're cute. Or maybe you're in trouble." She turns to walk away, then looks over her shoulder and raises an eyebrow, "Do you want to see the city or not?"

She feels a wave of neurons pulse through her, but she cannot pinpoint the feeling. Is it embarrassment? Nervousness? Or is she feeling aroused by this girl? After an awkward pause, she registers the question and follows without saying a word.

"You can call me Crystal," the girl says without looking at her. When she does not respond, Crystal asks, "And what can we call you?"

"What's in a name?" she asks, never understanding why people still use names or why they ever did.

"We'll call you Desertia then," she says, waving over the boys. "This is our new girl, Desertia. Desertia, this is Hauns, Rob and Sanders." The boys all look her up and down to intimidate her, but she does not give into the fear of uncertainty. She nods, and they all get back to work, picking up their loads and walking through the alleys.

What's in a name?
Does your name "fit" you or do you resonate with something else?

Crew

"We saw you coming from the seventh floor," Crystal explains, "It's not difficult to spot something moving in empty spaces."

The guys drop to a distance behind the girls, chatting about the artifacts they found in the office, so she focuses on observing her new city guide. Crystal has a strong attitude about her and although she cannot distinguish it, there is something about her she feels her Self attracted to.

"What has it been like living in the city?"

"The only thing that remains the same is the nightlife," Crystal responds with a wink, "and that's why we've stayed."

She melts, almost letting the words pass through one ear to the next, reliving the wink again and again. Is it her confidence or her self-expression she finds so attractive? Her awareness of this unjustified interest in Crystal heightens. She must remain on guard and not get distracted—she does not know a stranger.

"Everyone has their crew, this is mine minus some," Crystal points to the guys. "The place seems completely empty during the day, but at night it's crawling with those who stayed and those who come for goods to trade. We entertain ourselves with unlocked doors and shattered windows. You never know what or who you'll find in there. Are you staying the night? Check it out for yourself!"

Crystal dashes forward, turning to run backwards, then opening her arms wide and spinning around the alley with vibrant laughter. The guys whistle and shout, Hauns drops his things and chases after her, picking her up over his shoulder and spinning her around. They spin slower to a stop, and he sets her down, both laughing and panting. She throws her arms around his neck and hugs him tight.

The other two boys approach from behind, and, to her surprise, she does not feel threatened by them anymore. Beneath the hard and cold, pure love surrounds her. If she could just break through the guarded Self, perhaps she would feel love within too. As the creator of her own reality, she softens her gaze and peers at the gentle giants standing on either side. They both smile beautiful smiles at her.

Suddenly, her body takes off in Crystal's direction and she finds herself spinning too. The guys join, and soon everyone is laughing and spinning, until they collapse into a supportive embrace.

She experiences a flashback to the moment the boy handed her back the rock, leaving her inner child to forever be a solo artist. Her interest in the youthful souls of these strangers sparks, and the mind plays with ideas and visions. Open minds and open hearts, pure inner children. She is excited to see where their curiosity will take them.

Can you identify your own first-impression persona?

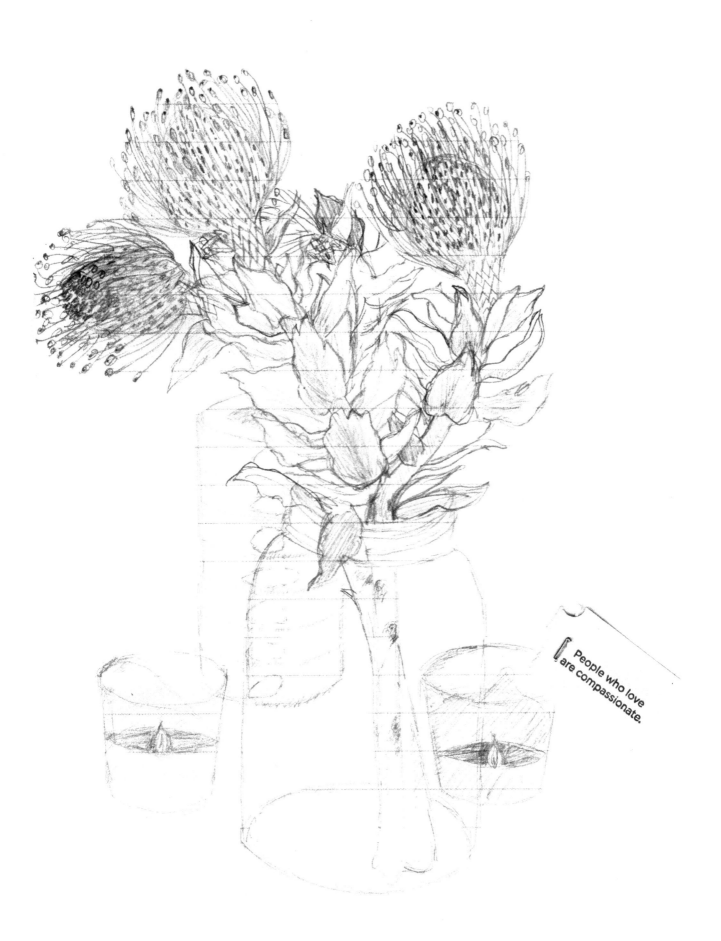

People who love
are compassionate.

Everything is coming together now

Return

She agrees to stay the night with this new crew in their home, an abandoned building. The ninth floor where they reside is rather luxurious with all kinds of treasures retrieved from abandoned homes and buildings. Art, pottery, and textiles decorate the living space organically, not organized but tossed into their perfect place.

They are greeted by two girls, Labora and Roxy, and three guys, Reg, Lexi, and Dime. Crystal grabs her by the hand, and introduces her to everyone as Desertia. Everyone is welcoming, enthusiastic to meet her and curious to hear about her desert journey. Crystal recognizes that Desertia is overwhelmed by the sudden sensory overload, and excuses her for a house tour.

One room, which is missing an outer wall completely, was a garden area. Crystal explains it gets the most sun, and they built vegetable beds from wood scraps around the junkyards. With no access to running water, their garden failed and they have adapted to trading and city foraging from buildings and houses. They have a plentiful stock of canned goods collected from their mission trips.

Another room is a studio space, where they collaborate on projects, such as making clothes or, if they are lucky enough to obtain the right materials, an art project. She thinks about her journal and pencil, how lucky she is to receive Life's gifts that inspire creativity and reflective thought.

The last room is filled front to back with mattresses, blankets and pillows.

"This is where we sleep," Crystal says, straightening one of the blankets out, "and other things." With that same wink, she pulls Desertia into the room gently and across the mattresses to the back corner of the room, where they sit with their backs propped against the walls facing one another. "How are you feeling?"

Desertia closes her eyes to check in with her Self, feeling open in Crystal's presence. "Like the air is carrying me, because Life is too fast for me to walk. Like a child, exploring the world with no previous knowledge. I feel really... enticed by you." She opens her eyes to Crystal's prideful grin. Her dark hair falls over her shoulders.

"Welcome home, sweet spirit," she says, wrapping her arms around Desertia's neck as she did to Hauns, their bodies melting into one another with a loud sigh. "Our souls have interlaced many times, and I always know when you return, because you bring such calm energy. You radiate it so far that I knew you were coming today."

She recognizes the same panicked feeling arising within her as when the boy suggested they knew each other from past lives. "Why does everyone think they know me?" Desertia asks her Self. Her enjoyment in remaining a mystery to strangers reflects her ego, and she chooses to let go of her stubbornness so this connection can flourish.

Do you prefer to be a mystery, an open book, or a balance of both?
Is this preference one of the ego—an act of protection?

Around the Table

Dime calls for the girls to join the crew for dinner. Crystal straightens up, placing her hands on Desertia's shoulders, and gives her a reassuring smile, "May the wind carry you gently."

They walk over the mattresses and into the living space, where everyone gathers around an office table, sitting on swivel chairs. "Desertia, you can take my chair for tonight. We will get another one tomorrow for you," Roxy says patting the seat next to her and squeezes in with Reg.

Although sitting on the floor helps her feel grounded, she nods gratefully, putting her palms together at her heart, a gesture of gratitude. Roxy returns the gesture first, and then they all do.

Dinner is a salad of leafy greens, peppers, and canned tuna. Rob pounds his fists on the table with excitement before pulling out his bag, revealing a jar of green olives. She admires each of them as their eyebrows lift with excitement, some of their mouths gaping open—obviously a rare find. "Bro, you are like a hound always sniffing out the best foods!" Reg shouts, throwing up his hand for a high five.

The olive jar floats around the table, and when it gets to her, she passes it without taking any. Noticeably offended, Rob says, "Girl, you can't be picky around here. You have to eat to survive!"

She gently responds with a soft smile, "I really appreciate your generosity, but you don't need to worry about me."

Roxy passes the jar along and tells Rob to mind his own business, so he just huffs and shakes his head, taking the jar. When the salad comes around, Desertia also passes it to Roxy without serving herself.

"What gives?" Roxy asks.

"Mind your own business, Roxy," Rob mimics to her. She punches his shoulder and serves herself, offering one more time to serve Desertia as well.

"We don't actually have to consume anything, if we can get our energy directly from the Source. Just like we don't have to receive explanations in order to uncover answers, we only need to observe. But, if you must know, I don't eat," she says quietly, noticing her insecurities in being "odd."

Reg and Roxy look at one another, then they shrug their shoulders and continue passing the plate. She relaxes her shoulders, grateful there is no need to speak more than necessary.

When the dish is served, Crystal suggests they each go around and say something they are grateful for in this moment.

They all nod in compliance and she begins, "I am grateful to be connected deeper than what's possible in the physical to each of you. And for all that has had to happen to bring us here together—right here, right now."

Some "Amens" and claps go around the table, and everyone shares something: this food, this house, to be alive, the many gifts scattered around the city.

When it comes to Desertia, she closes her eyes to reconnect again with her Self. She can feel everyone's eyes staring at her as she reflects on the series of events leading her here, returning to her past-lives parked on the side of the road.

"I am grateful for awareness, for the ability to see my Self in each of you. I am grateful for each moment, aligning exactly as it is meant to for each and everyone one of us to grow towards our highest Self." She stops suddenly remembering whom she is with, and peeks through her right eye. "I am grateful for you opening up your home to me."

They all smile at her with the same admiration, as if she is sitting on a pedestal and they are all witnessing an angel for the first time. Roxy takes her hand and smiles, gazing deeply into her soul, "You are welcome here, sister."

They continue sharing until everyone is complete, then they begin eating, chatting about their adventures of the day. The other group had wandered east in the city to admire some old murals, and met a foreign trader with long hair and big eyes, who gifted them tobacco.

She smiles, knowing who the trader is, grateful to hear of his perseverance through this life, through his individual growth. Dime says they invited him back for dinner, but he politely declined so he could prepare for the market tonight.

"Did he have anything worthwhile?" Sanders asks with wide eyes.

"Nothing we thought we might need, but you can check again tonight," Lexi says.

Desertia thinks about their meeting at the trading post, his dance with the stone. Sometimes you do not think you need something until you discover all its possibilities.

"Are we headed somewhere tonight?" Desertia asks anxiously. Is she going to have to face this boy again?

"Every night," Lexi says with a devilish smile, "There will be music, laughter, and we can introduce you to the community!"

Desertia shifts uncomfortably in her seat, still unsure how to distinguish excitement from anxiety. Her stomach gives life to wings, butterflies fluttering around. The body is heating up, specifically in her hands and face. She plans her escape and disguise. The boy, with his heavy load, is not likely to find her on the dance floor.

What are you grateful for?

63

Mind's Eye

Nightfall is upon them, and she can feel the energy increasing as the girls dress up and the boys smoke rolled tobacco. She sits in meditation until everyone is ready. Her insecurities about being different resurface—her dirtied clothes, quietness, and desire to be alone. She feels more isolated now than she ever did alone.

The girls start to appear, Labora wearing a sky-blue mini skirt paired with a white belt and tank top. The colors compliment her red hair and pale skin, the skirt revealing her skinny legs. Roxy sports Crystal's red top from earlier with high-waist faux leather shorts. Her brown hair is tied in a loose bun on top of her head, some strands falling to shape her high cheekbones. She notices their rib cages now, and wonders if it has always been this way for them in the city.

Crystal appears a couple minutes later wearing a sparkly gold mini dress and short black boots, and heads over to the crew. The guys compliment the girls, checking them up and down. Crystal places her arm around Dime's shoulders, and Desertia watches as Dime runs his hand gently down Crystal's back and over her curves, all the while staring up at her golden eyes. Crystal laughs confidently, running her fingers through his hair, before looking around, realizing the crew is not complete yet.

Knowing Crystal is looking for her, Desertia closes her eyes and pretends to meditate again. Footsteps approach her, "Let's spice you up, little lady," Crystal says, pulling Desertia off the floor gently, calling to Roxy and Labora for assistance in the closet.

The hall closet is filled with clothes, and they start digging through the pile, holding a couple items to Desertia's chest and waist before agreeing on a silky white slip dress. She feels Crystal lift her tank top from her belly button and slowly slip it over her shoulders. The contrast between being bare in the cool concrete rooms and Crystal's warm breath on her neck sends chills down the body.

The other girls watch from the bed, exchanging smiles and jaw drops as she transforms from a desert rat to a bedroom angel. Roxy hops up with a tortoise clip, running her fingers through Desertia's hair, clipping it into a loose bunch in the back.

Suddenly she feels so pampered, so connected with these strangers. The level of comfort they have with one another is opening her heart to sisterhood. They all come together in embrace, their giggles as pleasurable to Desertia as the birds chirping, and she realizes all connection and relatedness can only be lost from the mind's eye. Life is always connecting her with people, but the mind does not experience connection like the body and soul.

Labora swings the closet door open to reveal Desertia's reflection in a long mirror. Other than shattered windows in the city, which she intentionally breezed by, she has not seen her reflection since she abandoned her car. She barely recognizes the skinny creature staring back at her. Dressed up, standing in front of the gawking eyes of this sisterhood, she feels magical, beautiful, as if her vessel is finally a mirror image of her Self, her soul.

Do you experience connection in the mind, body, or spirit?

64

blissful isolation
is finding
peace in
the idea of
nothing

what would
you do if
you found
yourself alon
with your
imagination?

Night Crawlers

For the second time, the girls emerge from the bedroom and the guys exchange looks with one another. Desertia begins to feel uncomfortable as Hauns approaches her, remembering what her father told her at fourteen, "Guys just want to have sex with you." Here she is, vulnerable in a slip, surrounded by guys, with no father to protect her.

"You look beautiful," he says sweetly, then turns to the rest of the crew and asks, "Aren't these ladies bangin'?" She finds it comical, the language exchange between genders. The slang, the content, all tailored to the receiver. Nothing has changed, except she feels more comfortable witnessing the authenticity of it.

"Let's go! We're gonna be late," Reg yells to everyone. Desertia laughs to her Self, does time still exist in the cities? She grabs the Magic Bag, which jingles loudly on her back.

They pile down the stairs to the concrete floors of Phoenix and begin moving through the dark. Everyone is holding someone's hand, and they skip playfully through the streets. She is still not sure where they are going, but does anyone?

Desertia notices her Self floating between true enjoyment and having to remember to enjoy the experience, as the mind attempts to isolate her from the rest through comparison. Her excitement for the party does not match everyone else's and she wonders if she looks as magnetic as the other girls who receive compliments and physical touch from the guys. The sound of her bells and reconnecting with her newly discovered sisters through smiles and laughter are her only means to re-center.

The night has taken over the sky, the only thing lighting the way is the moon, and they see no people along the way. Eventually, they arrive at a small hill on the city's outskirts and climb up old wooden steps. The darkness brightens up to a small valley nestled into the rolling hills. There is fire, loud voices, instruments, and thirty souls scattered below her on the dance floor, browsing vendors, and making music.

She freezes, surprised that something like this might still exist. The crew begins running down the slope toward the party, flowing directly into dance with the drummers.

As if watching a child dance for the first time, she laughs with excitement to see the body move in a way it has not since the pandemic annihilated gatherings. It waves, spins, drops and rises again to the drumbeat, the music resilient, a survivor.

Her vessel carries her, and she can feel all things flowing through her. She is surprised how it can move, how it can be so independent without her telling it what to do. Then Desertia loses her Self in the flow, closing her eyes and moving alone. Every sensation, every drum beat, a dose of pure ecstasy.

She loves to be lost—in moments, conversations, and unfamiliar places—because where she cannot even find her Self, she is hidden from Life's obstacles.

Within which activity(s) do you experience flow and how does it feel?

Masks

"Desertia, come with us!" Crystal shouts, as Dime pulls her along in an attempt to catch up with the crew.

The body moves without question, until her fingers link up with Crystals. The sensations are still flowing, and Crystal's smile never looked as beautiful and happy as it does to be side by side with Desertia. They catch up with the rest of the crew in a quieter space away from the music, fire pits roaring.

Mingling begins with fellow city dwellers, and she feels the body sink into the calm and quiet, staring intensely into the roaring fire and listening to the conversations around her. Crystal and Dime are whispering nearby, and when she breaks her gaze from the flames, she sees them staring at her. They do not look away; they smile and wave her over.

The body does not get up, but instead crawls in her little white dress. She becomes aware of a bubbling energy, promiscuity, coming over her. It is not her creation, but the body reacts and plays into the crawl. She recognizes the carnal look of sensual excitement in their eyes. Power overtakes her discomfort, and the mind discovers confidence in her strut — or the strut of her character.

Crystal pulls Desertia onto her lap, hugging her tight from behind. Dime lights a cigarette, never taking his eyes off the girls. His cool gaze offers a peek behind the veil of humanity, and she sees his lust and desire burning like the tip of the cigarette. He wears a mask, but struggles to keep it aligned on his face.

Dime passes Desertia the lit roll, and she inhales deeply, depriving her lungs of oxygen to get high. She feels Crystal tracing the lines of her neck to her collarbone, shoulders down to wrists and fingertips, up the front of her chest from the sternum. Watching Dime's reaction, Desertia wonders if Crystal is trying to please her or Dime.

Sinking deeper into the sensations of tobacco smoke rushing throughout the body, she naturally passes it along to Dime, who is now lying with his head on her lap, Desertia's fingertips running through his curly black hair.

How did they get here? How can she be so consciously aware of her fears around intimacy, so aware of human tendencies to crave, yet so easy to take the bait? She has not smoked anything since before the pandemic, purifying the body for healing, and now she feels her Self drifting through her own veins, a victim to the temptations, but a warrior against resistance.

Like a dream, she has no control over the situation. The body wants what the mind is afraid of, and the soul must watch the horror film. All she can do is accept it, discover enjoyment in it; otherwise, she will suffer from Life's experiences.

What does your body want that your mind doesn't, and vice versa?
Can you discover gratitude in these moments of disconnect?

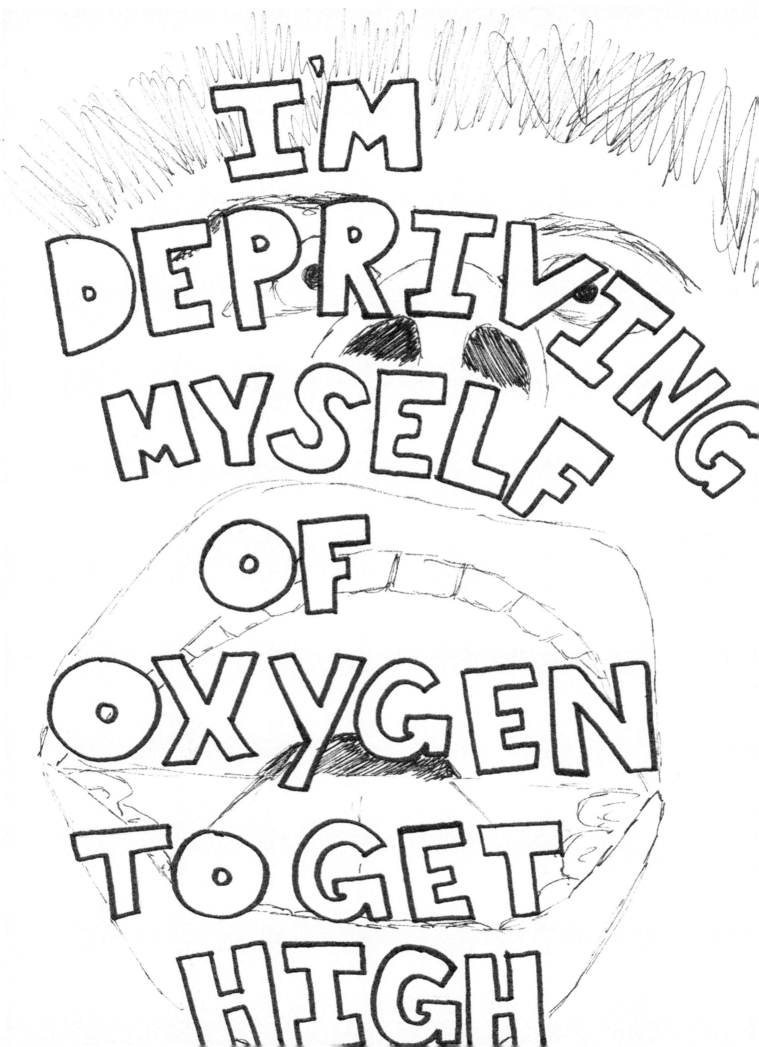

Overlap

A hand shakes her outstretched leg, and she jolts back protectively, her guarded Self. Hovering over her is the familiar face of a young man, the one she met at the trading post and abandoned in his sleep.

"Hey! What're you doing here?" he shouts over the music, "I almost didn't recognize you in this dress!"

Guilt rushes over her immediately, knowing that they both know a pain from the last meeting—or parting. He is wearing baggy rainbow-dyed pants, shirtless.

"I almost didn't recognize you without the baggage," she responds with a smile, "Join us, these are my friends Crystal and Dime."

"Pleasure to meet you! And what's your name?" Crystal asks with eyes squinted, a bit faded from the smoke.

The boy glances at Desertia, then at Crystal, and mocks, "What's in a name anyway?"

Crystal laughs with amusement. Dime steps in, "We actually met recently in the city. Do you remember me?"

"Sure I do," he says resting his gaze on Desertia, "And I believe in the importance of meeting a person twice. My name is Rio, by the way."

Feeling a draft come up her dress, she adjusts her seated posture. He clearly is not upset with her, just happy to be reunited on this winding spiral of a Life. Taking out and lighting a rolled cigarette, he squats down next to them, and she wonders if he can sense how she is feeling.

Desertia's silence, although comforting for her, inspires Crystal to strike up a conversation about trading, and Desertia just observes him as the two souls connect. He appears to be wearing the same mask, a nearly disintegrated cover for the hurt he feels within from many past lives of abandonment.

Desertia wonders what her mask looks like and how others perceive it and uses Rio as a reflection tool. She is often complimented on her graciousness, calmness, and beauty. Underlying that is a desire to be acknowledged, appreciated, and accepted.

Who could love her shadows, the insecurity of separateness? Desertia must wear her mask at all times, unleashing the veiled face only in moments of self-sabotage.

She imagines an unveiled Self, releasing the pain of loneliness, which sits dormant underneath the mask for a lifetime, if not many lifetimes.

Consider the ways other see you… What mask(s) do you wear?
Do you see your Self the same way?

Journal Entry 4

Dear Moraine,

What is your "love language"? I have been resisting acceptance, but mine is "words of affirmation."

It's been brought to my attention repeatedly on this journey that I have repressed many, if not all of my, emotions throughout my life, resulting in the inability to cry or yell, as well as feeling extreme happiness and satisfaction. There are few occasions where I have a breakthrough.

A mentor of mine asked me to repeat, "I love myself," or any positive affirmation. What I thought would come out as a direct, positive statement actually felt embarrassing, as my confident tone did not match my immediate eye dart.

My mentor pointed this out, and I realized my whole life had been shaped by others expectations and opinions of me—I could not think for my Self. But now I can.

Now, I am still curious to know how I show up in the world, but from a place of self-awareness.

If everyone is a reflection of me, then I am a reflection of them. If I am the manifester, creator, of my own experience, then I have the ability to shape my Self into the form I want to see in others: someone of confidence, internal and external love, gratitude, and wisdom.

I am the mask that people wear, so what face and lens do I want to offer to others?

Please, allow me to guide, inspire and transform my Self; therefore, everyone else can live in the same freedom of expression and knowing.

You are the mask that people wear. What face & lens do you want to offer to others?

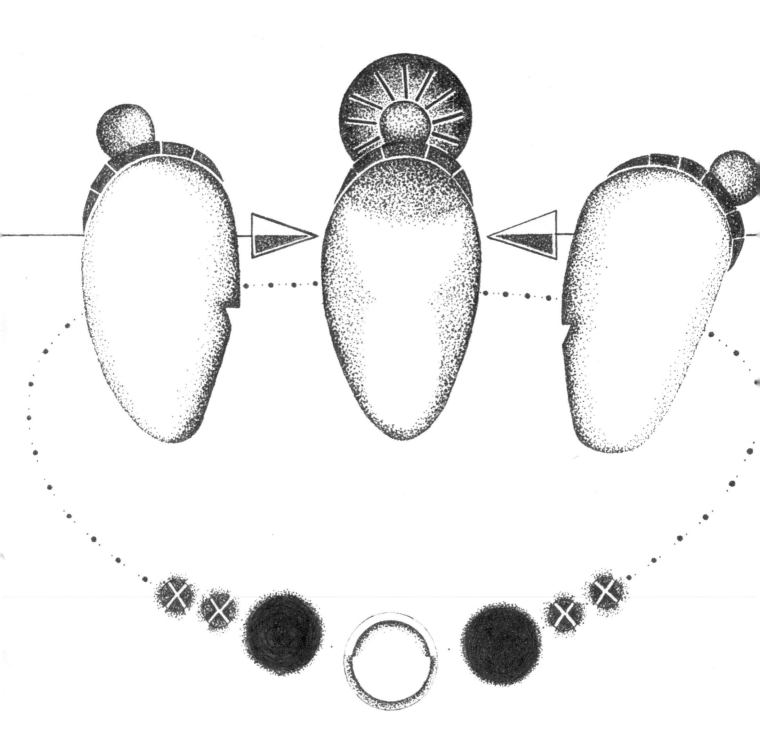

Confrontations

The night continues with more conversation than she had experienced in the months alone. She finds the small talk boring, without intention or direction, and she observes her Self drifting between longing for silence and reassuring her Self that this is exactly where she is meant to be. In the process, she discovers gratitude for all experiences.

Crystal yawns, and she wonders if it is fake or not. It makes no difference, because she stands up implying she is heading home, Dime getting up to follow her. Crystal smiles an inviting smile, extending her hand out to Rio. Desertia and Rio look at each other, then stand up simultaneously holding hands.

Dime takes Crystal's other hand in one, Desertia's in another. The exposure to physical touch triggers her fears of intimacy. The fear is nothing new, but this experience and her awareness of Self are.

She reminds her Self to find gratitude and peace in the present moment. Nothing bad has to happen, as least if she remains open to a positive experience. Their hands remain locked the entire walk home, over the hill and back into the dark cityscape.

Dime and Crystal head first up the stairwell and Rio tugs her hand gently, indicating for her to stay back with him. The body tenses, but she knows it is only scared of the Truth, what every moment of confrontation brings. He smiles at her softly, as if to reassure her.

"Desertia, sit and talk with me before I leave."

Her heart is open, the mind aware.

"I know why you left that night, and I just want you to know I am not upset with you. I couldn't be," he says, gazing into her open heart.

"Thank you," she says, returning the gaze, "I am not surprised our paths have crossed again."

"That's how it goes with unfinished business, and I told you, you have a gift for me."

Her heart sinks, wondering if he is only pretending to connect with her on some false agenda, like every other man in her life. Desertia closes her eyes to better see what the story playing in her head roots into.

The black shades behind her eyelids warp into an image: shackles on her ankles and wrists, arms pulled behind her back. She understands now that she is trying to run from this gift, her purpose to heal others. Only when she gives the gift will she be set free.

What is holding you back?
What do you need to give in order to be set free?

73

Shackles

"Desertia!" Crystal shouts down the staircase, "After party upstairs if you two want to join!"

She opens her eyes to see Rio, his eyes digging to see what is going on inside the mind. Her eyes are soft with apology and forgiveness. Desertia takes his hand in hers and takes a big inhale, closing her eyes once again. She searches the vast darkness for a clue on what to give him. Dark rain clouds travel over a toddler, stranded naked in the desert.

Desertia wants to hug him, to let him know he is not alone, that he is safe. She slides her arms under Rio's and embraces him tightly, sharing her warmth. She feels the body relax in his arms and, through unexpected exchange of security, he holds her like her father did. For protecting one another, she is grateful.

They drop their arms, turning to head up the stairs. As they climb higher, many voices emerge and she realizes the whole family is home, plus friends.

Everyone is smiling or laughing, sprawled across the mattresses, using one another's body as a pillow, holding hands, engaging in many conversations. Desertia analyzes Rio's face, smiling at how honest his expression of surprise and suspicion are, like this is an unusual occurrence to see humans experiencing intimacy in this way.

As she searches for Crystal, she spots some fondling, caressing, and kissing going on between couples, sometimes even three or more people. Desertia does n0t recognize all the faces, and she darts her stare quickly, feeling invasive for staring at all. Crystal and Dime are snuggled up in a corner, sharing stories from the evening with Sanders and Labora.

Crystal lifts her gaze, but rather than waving with her usual excitement, she pulls the two bodies from the door with her eyes, until they are seated in the corner. She can feel her Self being taken over, losing control under Crystal's magnetism. Crystal shifts from Dime, snuggling up against Desertia, holding her hand and kissing it softly, resting her feet on Dime, who smiles at the girls with his usual excitement.

Images of shackles appear again, but she is connected to nothing. Self-enslavement.

She sets her Self free, if only for this moment, and positions her back against Rio's chest, Crystal's head falling perfectly in the inner crevice of Desertia's arm. She runs her fingers through Crystal's hair, attempting to focus on Labora's story about how she felt love at first sight with one of the drummers from the event.

Questioning the Truth about such an occurrence, she looks around at everyone surrounding her, what does it feel like—love? She stares intentionally at every individual, trying to think of what she loves about them, realizing the depth of their relationship is too shallow for her love to go beyond the surface. How can love at first sight be real?

Describe qualities of love…
What does it take to love someone?

Accept the things you can't control

do you
want to
know the
secret to
successes?

every one
is on their
own path
at their
own pace.
let what
is, be.

Manifestation

Pondering the concept of Love, Desertia nearly misses Rio sharing that his wife and son live in what used to be known as the Grand Canyon with other families, where he is heading at sunrise. He talks about his love for his family, the community, and how he would walk in freezing temperatures some nights to hit a trading post by early morning, in search of one thing for the community, without even knowing what he might find.

This time, an elder is very sick, and he came to the trading post in hopes of finding an herbalist or someone who can heal the elder. Rio mentions the elder is one of the original founders of the community and the peacemaker when there is dispute.

"I'm not sure what will become of the community if he passes. There is no one who can heal quite like he can."

Desertia can hear the sadness in his voice, a dam in the river of his tears, the longing for peace and unity. The mind is lost in visuals of the elder, what she imagines Rio's wife and baby look like, the weight that sits on his shoulders as a provider for extended family.

When she brings her attention back to reality, she realizes she is tracing shapes onto his black jean shorts, and she shames her Self for even laying against this married man and father. Embarrassed, Desertia wonders if she was wrong in thinking they were connecting on a romantic level. She shakes the thought out of her head, remembering she is more like a mother to a child than a romantic partner for him.

Crystal suggests the group should do a quick manifestation prayer for Rio's family, and they take turns sharing what they are manifesting for him on his journey.

"I manifest you find a powerful healer that comes with you on your journey home, bringing lots of medicine, but more importantly peace," Crystal says.

"I manifest your family can find peace without one person having to hold it all together," Dime says.

"I manifest so much love and wisdom flourishes in that canyon, healing all of the chaos at once," Sanders says.

They look at her, waiting for her to manifest something for him and she freezes. If she can manifest anything for him, it is that he is freed from the weight, however that plays out, and she worries about coming off as insensitive. Her eyes roll up to the ceiling pondering how she can word it differently, when Rio steps in.

"I appreciate all your prayers and, while Desertia meditates on this, I'd like to manifest something. I manifest that everyone, all of us that remain, find inner peace, so we can be peaceful without. I manifest that my community does not stay 'my' community, but expands outward to connect with other families.

I manifest a life of love and unity. Freedom." He looks at her, putting her back on the main stage.

Desertia feels tears starting to burn behind her eyes in resonation with his manifestation. She has always prayed for life like this. She has wondered if it was this exact manifestation that caused the death of so many people—those who could not adapt fast enough to the shifts, the crumbling of so many societies, the rebirth necessary to obtain something so out of reach in a long-gone, corrupt world. She knows the people who remain share something in common—a collective gift.

Crystal squeezes her hand and kisses the inside of her bicep, "It's okay, Desertia, you're safe to be and say whatever is coming up."

She suddenly remembers where she is, that if her words result in disaster, the desert is just around the corner to welcome her home. The mind is flooding, like a broken dam, with the Truth of what everyone is manifesting. She can see the future, the manifested form of these prayers. The difficulty of what she is trying to put into words makes her nauseous.

"I manifest…" she starts with tears slowly leaking from her eyes, "…that I can discover… what it means to love, to unite, so I can be…" she pauses to take a deep breath. "So I can be the healer for you and your family." She chooses each word with the utmost care.

Looking up to meet Rio's eyes Desertia says, "You said I have a gift for you when we met at the trading post. I only carry one gift, one intention to heal, and I have yet to discover for myself how that manifests physically, but I do know you are leaving at sunrise... and I am coming with you."

They are all quiet for a moment, when Crystal chimes in, "Me too. You manifested unity of communities, of families. That sings to me—I want that too."

Dime chimes in, followed by Sanders and Labora, and the message is traveling through the room that everyone is leaving at sunrise.

Desertia looks up at Rio, wishing she had the key to his mind, so fixated on how he might be perceiving the world at all times. He smiles at her, pulling her head close to his chest and kissing the top of her head, "You are an angel."

Reflecting on his comment as she sinks into his beating heart, Desertia feels as though she has just taken on half his weight, the pressure building on top of her. How is she going to heal an elder, let alone a community? She remembers her unspoken prayer to free Rio of the weight, she did not think it would manifest onto her.

The mind is silenced by the spirit, her Self, filling the vessel she was given the day she was born. She knows better than to let the mind manifest failure, upset. She knows it is that involuntary habit of thinking that has held her back from sharing her gift as a healer, a true angel. What she has yet to receive, she is unable to give to another.

Do you see, within the context of your life, where you may have manifested failure, upset?

Baby

Nobody sleeps. Chatter about the journey travels in waves through the room, a conversation starting at one wall moves across the sea of reclined bodies.

They plan to take all their belongings, every dress, every skateboard, every sentimental knick-knack, some fantasizing, others intentionally manifesting about how their new home will look and who they will meet in this merging of communities.

Desertia is grateful to carry so little on this journey. The pressure to make a difference for the lives of the canyon is enough for her. Thoughts of slinking off into the desert during the night pop up, and instead of pushing them away, she holds onto her options, more weight.

Talk turns to action until everyone is out of the room, loading bags, strapping anything and everything onto their bodies. She and Rio stay laying down, her head still resting on his chest, his arm around her back, holding her tightly. She has never experienced so much intimacy outside of sex, so much love unbound by the four walls of expectations. The word "boyfriend" pops up on the back of her eyelids. How pleased she is to not live in that world anymore, the world of ownership, and instead be in this transcended world, where friends kiss friends, and love is not exclusive.

His body twitches beneath her, and she tilts her head back to see if Rio is asleep. Desertia remembers the night when he slept on her lap so graciously, so vulnerably. A child. It excites her to be able to see him again in this state, because she finds so much peace and comfort in it, feeling most connected to him when he is the child.

As she admires his long eyelashes folded over his water lines and his lips touching effortlessly, as if resting on one another, the same way she is laying weightlessly on top of him, she is reminded of the heavy weight they now share. As long as they can lean on one other, the weight seems bearable.

In this freedom, this gentleness, she sees her Self in his baby face, her own inner child. The child shrinks into a fetus, resting gently against the walls of a mother's womb, which is strong in protecting the baby under many layers of heaviness threatening to smash the fetus at any moment the womb becomes weak.

Desertia wants to peel back the layers, to dig them up with a shovel, to give the womb space to rest. Surely, the child is affected by the stress the womb is taking on, even if it appears to be weightless, floating in a preserving liquid.

Remembering the baby is her, she feels a sense of security. No matter how much weight she takes on in this life, she is preserved and protected by Life, the womb and all its efforts.

Close your eyes, inviting your inner child to speak with you.
Ask, "How are you affected by the stress, the heaviness?"

comfort the child within

seek the child without

your numbing
yourself. quit
numbing yourself.
your numbing
yourself. quit
numbing yourself.
your numbing
yourself. quit
numbing yourself.
your numbing
yourself. quit
numbing yourself.
I'm numbing
myself. I love
numbing myself.

Weightless

As if Rio can sense Desertia staring at him sleep, he smiles, lips pressing together, before even opening his eyes. As he stirs back to waking state, she feels their weights clashing, holding together as if they are the source of gravity, and if they release the tension, their bodies will drift upward forever.

His transition from dreams to "reality" is one of the most beautiful, yet devastating, things she has ever seen, like ocean waves crashing madly against a rock wall and pulling the Earth into itself.

She wishes for him that he could return to blissful sleep, rather than having to face the world and his responsibilities.

It dawns on her that just as they are the survivors of the pandemic, she is a "chosen one"; therefore, she did not get to choose. And the perceived freedom she saw in the emptiness, the crumbling of governmental institutions, and release from the grid, is only an illusion. The illusion lies in the idea that she is free from responsibility, from inherited guilt, shame, and ways of being, free from expectations.

Yet, there is no authority, and Desertia still feels guilty for giving Rio hope, shame for lying on his chest when his wife and child are expecting him to return home alone, expected to do more than she is comfortable doing, and responsible for all of it.

Does real freedom exist? What even is freedom? She used to think it was having a lot of money and a job that required little time, so she could float around without a care and pursue her creativity and imagination.

Now, there is no money, no time, no job, and she still does not feel free.

Rio flutters his eyes open slowly as the sun begins peeking through the window, sharing his smile so generously with her and rubbing her back. "You were in my dream," he says in a sleepy voice, "We were standing on top of a mountain and this intense wind was blowing your hair around in all directions. Each strand got longer, until they were the length of the world.

You wrapped me tightly in some curls, while the rest of your hair webbed to the trees, lifting us off the ground, climbing upward. The strands clung to anything, the clouds and the stars, until we could not climb any higher. We sat in total darkness, yet we could stare into each other's eyes. It was there that I realized we are the light…"

It is so beautiful, his mind, and she cannot help but wonder if he heard her thinking about freedom. She longs to be in total darkness, emptiness, and weightlessness with him, to be free. She concludes she wishes to be dead.

What is "freedom" to you?

Free

Crystal enters the bedroom and snuggles on the other side of Rio, bringing herself face-to-face with Desertia on his chest. Crystal smiles, but Desertia can tell there is something Crystal is looking for in her eyes.

"How are you feeling?" Crystal asks.

She ponders for a moment, tuning into the body's emotional sensations. She has just wished death upon her Self, and although it means freedom, she feels uncomfortable and saddened by the only solution she can find.

"I feel… empty… and at the same time heavy," she concludes, feeling Rio shift uncomfortably beneath them.

Crystal gently entangles her fingers through Desertia's hair. She does not have anything to offer in words, so she holds a soft gaze. Crystal's eyes are filled with compassion, abundant love, and empathy.

Desertia feels some of the weight lift off the body, as if Crystal is asking to carry some of it. When she looks up at Rio, he is already staring at her with the same tender eyes. She is surprised by the warm tears beginning to roll down her cheeks, and nobody moves to hug her, rub her back, or wipe her tears. Nobody tells her it is okay or asks what is wrong.

Instead, they allow her to be exactly as she is in this very moment, never taking their loving expressions down.

She does not sob or whimper, her breathing does not even change, the tears just roll, and she lets them. When the tears dry, staining her cheeks, and the eyes feel empty, Crystal says, "You are so beautiful to be with, Desertia. We have a long walk ahead of us. If you feel heavy, like you need to let more weight go, just look down at your hands and know you have us to hold you."

Desertia looks up at Rio, who nods in agreement with Crystal. She hugs them both tightly, burying her head into Rio's soft shirt, relishing in the lightness she was longing for, being supported by a family, connected with the masculine and feminine.

How do you react to another's emotions?

Journal Entry 5

Dear Moraine,

Does everyone experience these thoughts, these self-criticisms?

These people all seem so confident, so secure. I am surrounded by beautiful individuals, in and out. Surely, there's someone sitting next to me looking around, asking the same questions, in judgment of themselves and others, thinking those things we only ever think to ourselves.

I'm sure there is something about the close bond between two people that reveals these critical egos, thoughts you don't hear until the heart slips up in loving trust and in comfort.

I am far away from my neighbor, whose knees and shoulders brush up against mine. Far from ever truly hearing them. So far away, their heartbeat is silent amongst the white noise.

To be aware of the silence, the white noise lingering between and behind every spoken word, is to be aware of one's feelings. It's the key to the shackles of those you love. I hear their vibrations, their unspoken words, and I respond with compassion, with love, with an open mind and open heart.

When I ride these waves, I am suddenly a part of the flood that washes through their mind, their heart, down their spine, circulating through every tendon. I realize, all this time, we've been speaking the same language. In fact, we all speak the same language—the unspoken language. I realize we don't need the shackles' key to give our compassion, love, open mind and open heart.

The way Rio and Crystal listen to me, not using a key or any tool to break in, inspires me to open up, and it leaves me feeling empowered in my choice to do so.

I'd like to practice what I learned from them, to create space for the healing process and inspire self-awareness.

Please, help me hold this space by reminding me before I speak.

How deeply do you know your friends, your family?
How deep do they know you?

Balance

The house is nearly empty, even the mattresses have been tied together on a makeshift trolley. She is feeling antsy, secretly impatient. "Take your time," she says repeatedly, as some in the group individually apologize to her and Rio, who have been packed and ready to go since before the pandemic began.

Desertia and Rio sit together, backs resting against their bags in the living space, watching everyone determine what leaves and stays, where it goes if it is making it on the journey, and who will carry it to start. Their bodies moving at a sloth's pace, their minds frantic with this major shift.

Rex tells Desertia that this is the first time they are moving since the pandemic started, having joined here together years ago, collecting and developing a comfortable communal space every day since. She begins to explore in her own life how she defines comfort, and what could have been comforting were she to live in a city, surrounded by things that give off this illusion of "comfort."

She remembers moving from city to city, country to country before the pandemic shut down the borders and established invisible walls. She was always so excited to wander through the new cities, sift through their thrift store treasures, taste their best restaurants, and explore a city's soul through the many art galleries.

It has been so long since she thought about those art galleries, and she wonders if any of the Phoenix art galleries are still intact, or if they were terrorized for the sake of bringing "comfort" to someone's home.

Finally, the time has come to leave. It is about noon now, and she stares at Rio's tired face, expressionless. She wonders if he is irritated by the wait, or if he is content.

"How are you feeling?" she asks him, placing a hand on his arm.

With a delayed snap of the neck, he faces her as if startled by her presence, "I am eager to get home."

Without his big smile, she feels disconnected from him, like strangers. She intends to feel compassion for his exhaustion and impatience, sinking into this new version of him. A sense of foolishness clouds her intentions, and she feels naive for thinking he was always one way: happy. He is a husband, a father, a tradesman, and a community caretaker, but, most of all, he is human.

The guys are working together to carry the mattress bundle vertically down the nine flights of stairs. Rio gets up to help, "Can you bring my bag down?" he asks her.

She nods, looking down at his large bundle on the floor. Can she? The bag probably weighs more than her, but she figures she can just let it roll down the flights of stairs if she has to. The girls meet in the living space, finishing their last round checking for any forgotten belongings.

Labora looks sad, exhausted, her face drooping as she looks around at their empty home. Crystal notices right away and gathers her in her arms for a hug. They stand there for a long time, eventually sobbing simultaneously. Grief.

Although Desertia does not feel connected to tangible items, she does know and understand the grieving process. It comes much quicker for the embodied feminine, seeking support from the foundational and strong masculine. It is beautiful, inspiring, to see the girls embody both in order to support one another.

Suddenly, she is reminded of the grey-haired goddess, the omen of the snake: masculinity. She reflects on the current context of her life, understanding now the balance of and transition between masculine and feminine, nature and nurture, sharing the weight of the world.

The girls gather for a group hug, and she stands up to join them, embracing them all from the outside, feeling her own masculinity and creating support for them all.

Desertia feels powerful, divine, standing in the presence of Life's most beautiful expressions, the many acts of love shared through this sisterhood, this family. Her many desires, or prayers, for this connection are being answered, and she starts laughing—of course she would discover it in the city.

The girls detangle, and Crystal asks her what she is laughing at.

"I think I just needed to release something," she says apologetically, not wanting to offend them or lose their trust. The laughter did seem to finalize the transcendence of isolation for her, to seal the deal. Balance has been experienced, successful.

They all smile at one another, grab their bags, and begin their descent down the stairs.

As expected, Rio's bag is much larger than she can carry, and she experiences a new level of respect, inspired by his strength, his foundation. Desertia sets the Magic Bag down on the floor to drag his bag across the room to the stairs, ignoring the jingling bells. She picks hers up once again, appreciating its weightlessness, confirms the girls are far enough ahead of her, then lets the weight tumble, clink, and bang as it topples down the concrete steps.

There is an unexpected empowerment in the strength to cause such a ruckus. To be loud, to be bold, to let something tumble, are in opposition to Desertia's ways of being delicate and quiet. She feels a wave of adrenaline carrying her down the flights of stairs, wondering if she has worked up the strength to carry the bag now. Will her power be lost in choosing to carry the bag instead of forcing it?

What gives you power?
How does it feel?

85

Grudging

When Desertia reaches the second to last flight, Rio appears around the corner just as she is preparing to shove the bag over the edge. His face is a mixture of concern and anger, and she freezes.

"What are you doing!" he shouts, "There are so many valuable things in this bag!"

Desertia feels immediately chastised by his outburst, her inner child screaming, wanting to run back up the stairs and hide within the walls of the empty rooms. Instead, the body cowers above him, unable to speak or move.

He stares at her for a moment, then moves up the stairs toward her. He snatches the bag up and displays an intense flash of resentment at her. Stupid, she felt. "I couldn't lift it," she musters.

"Then you tell me," he says quiet but stern, supporting the weight onto his crouched thigh, then over his back and onto his shoulders. He turns down the stairs, disappearing around the last corner. Desertia does not move, processing what has just happened. Did the others hear him yelling at her? Are they going to see her stupidity?

Remembering that he carries all of that weight calms her down. He must be fiery to truck the load across the desert, to be energized. And now he is exhausted. She is meant to be supporting his weight, not playing with it.

Awareness of the Self defrosts her. The body and mind are exhausted as well, and she forgives her Self for acting without consideration of another's things, Rio's attachment to the things he is bringing for and from his community. Behind her closed eyelids, a little girl sits in an empty room, crying. Desertia recognizes the child as her Self, and watches as her adult Self enters the room. The little girl looks up at her with big puppy eyes, her cheeks tear stained.

"I didn't mean to upset you," the young girl says to her older Self.

She knows there are no words that will share her compassion and love for this upset child, so instead she kneels by her side, and wraps her small body in her arms, rocking her back and forth. When the little girl is laughing again, Desertia releases her to stare into those big eyes.

It inspires her how children are not attached to one feeling, how they live without grudges. Although she is the adult, she is the student. Desertia carries on down the stairs, leaving the past at the top of the second floor.

Think of a child in your life…
Are they the student or you?

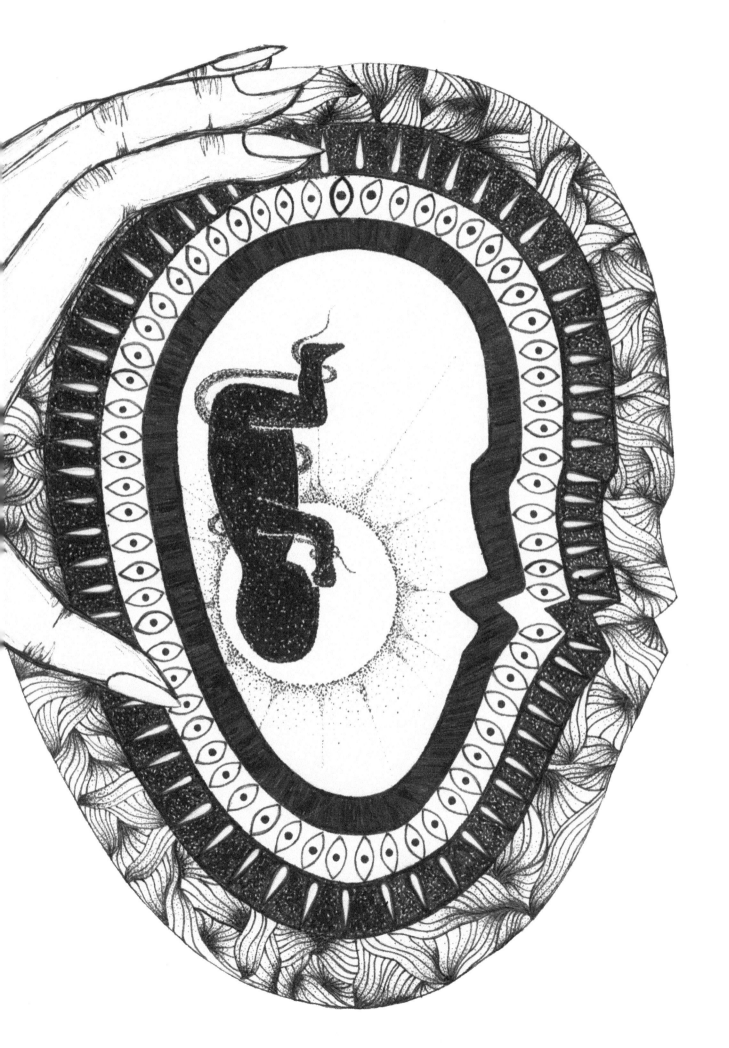

Family

On the ground floor, the group waits for her. When they see her appear, they begin loading their bags on their backs again. Rio smiles at her as if nothing is wrong, and she is grateful for his childishness.

The group is finally on their way, and she staggers behind them, admiring the deteriorating skyscrapers from bottom to top one last time. Is it a coincidence that the birthplace of her inner compass, the city, is the same environment where she connects now with family? It is as if the compass has been running her in circles all this time, leading her from one of Life's lessons to the next, just to lead her back home, where she can apply them.

They cross the dry riverbeds, once dammed, as the bridge's columns have crumbled making them impassable. The arroyo contains more trash than fossils, which is cemented into the dry dirt entangled with sun-cooked moss.

Rio falls back from the group to meet her as they pass small mountains to the east, telling Desertia a story about a party he attended early in the pandemic. "It felt like we lived in a bubble, where the virus couldn't touch us, and people called us ignorant."

"How many of your friends from that party are still alive?" she asks, trying not to cling to the incident on the stairwell.

"Most of us formed the community in the canyon, others went home to their families and were never heard from again. Nothing has changed within the community, we still like to party and make music. The dancing, the love, the laughter, that is what saved us. It kept us away from fear."

Desertia thinks about her bubble, how the vision of it alone wards off her own fears. It is easily understood why the community was so successful during the pandemic, considering they manifested a bubble around them, and she is eager to meet more of the like-minded individuals.

"What do you like most about the community?" she asks, curious to know as much as she can before their arrival.

"Well aren't you full of questions today?" he asks jokingly. He ponders the question for a moment, then shares, "Everyone is individual, yet everyone is One. There is ultimate freedom to be, the only encouragement being to heal. You choose your method."

"What are the methods available?"

"Great question! The discovery is what makes everyone unique as an individual. I'm curious to see what you come up with," he says excitedly.

"What did you come up with?" she asks.

"I really enjoy where your curiosity takes you," he says seriously this time. "There is something in walking long distances that allows me time and space to transform. I never return the same person, but I am not the one who notices the change."

She feels hesitant to ask anymore questions, realizing her guard has gone down, but the conversation is providing valuable insight into this stranger's perspective. She can assume it is the entire community or his wife that notices the change and, either way, she wants to know what shifts they experience in him.

Before she can ask her next question he says, "My turn to ask a question. How long have you been wandering on your own?"

She does not even know what day it is, let alone what day the destruction from the pandemic put her on her bare feet in the desert. "Long before the pandemic."

He struggles to ask a follow up question, and she notices how she sets others up in conversations that way. What's driving her from being so open and connected one minute, to completely detached and blocked the next?

When she looks up from the ground at him, he is giving her an expression that makes her wonder if he is reading her mind. His tongue is falling out of his mouth, head cocked, eyes rolled backward, as if to say "This kind of answer again? I'm bored and exhausted trying to crack your shell."

Nevertheless, he does not have to say anything. She understands if she wants to help anyone, if she wants to feel connected, she will have to trust and let go of this frequent switch in her way of being. "I've been walking alone since the gas stations stopped pumping gas into my car. But I am not sure the count of days," she answers in attempt to move over her Self, as if it is an obstacle.

"Where was that? Did you let your friends and family know?"

"It was outside of Salt Lake City, Utah, and I began wandering east to meet with them in the Midwest. Around Denver, I understood that anyone still attached to my childhood home by the time I got there would be involuntary, fatal. So I turned south to avoid the cold."

It has been a long time since she let her Self reflect on that day, let alone share it with someone else. She is reminded of the grief she experienced, feeling regretful for always being so detached from them. "Family" was more of a lesson than a blessing for her, and when she left the house at eighteen, she did not intend to return.

Up until that moment, she questioned why she had to be connected with the people who gave her life. Up until that moment, as far as she was concerned, she did not care if she ever saw them again.

Is family a group you are born into or did you discover family along your journey?

Double Life

The conversation continues exploring their background stories, the series of events that led them to this very moment. Desertia is aware that the surface-level questions have shifted from pre-pandemic—"What do you do for work? Where did you go to school? How old are you?"—to post-pandemic "What were you doing pre-pandemic and do you know where your friends and family are now?"

A question like this reveals a layer of the Self that no one could have imagined, like telling a friend you make as an adult about a high school experience. Essentially, one could say anything, be anything, re-create themselves and their story with every person they meet along the way.

What stings the most is the trust that is required—what must be surrendered. What would be the point of not believing what someone says? Never mind how crazy or unbelievable it may sound. The surrender reminds her of the numerous conversations she has shared about the many conceptions of God. Whether or not she believes what is being debated, there is no way to prove one way or another, and so she does not waste energy seeking any sort of evidence. She just lets the individual or group believe.

Through the conversation, Desertia discovers Rio is from Turkey, having moved to the United States at 14-years-old with his mother. His father had left their family for a mistress and his secret children—his double life.

She now understands the source of the hurt of his inner child. He is the wounded soldier of abandonment, out to make a difference and avoid being abandoned again by working hard to show his community the value in sticking together, sacrificing themselves for one another. Desertia understands she has been the opposite.

It was not her family who abandoned her, it was she who abandoned them, and it happened years before the pandemic. She abandoned the idea of them, "family," before she even physically abandoned them by moving out of the house. She gave up trying to relate to them, the black sheep.

Desertia's double life was sensational, the kind of pleasure one gets from a cigarette or a beer. The body vibrates, tingles, feels dizzy and euphoric, just to be brought down by the dissatisfying feeling it was trying to ditch in the first place. Everything temporary.

She was a lover to drugs, men, travel, and money. It did not matter who was with her or who was not, someone or something could always fill the space if she let them. They filled the space she assumed her family would have, were she to let them.

This time on her own has been healing the deep wound, which could never be mended by her addictions and escapes. Desertia struggles to share this with Rio, nervous he may see her the way he sees his father. She struggles with fear he may split her wounds open again, but she knows healing an open wound requires an open heart, and she is almost scabbing—nearing the end of the healing process.

Everyone has a wound… trust, abandonment, etc. Can you identify yours?

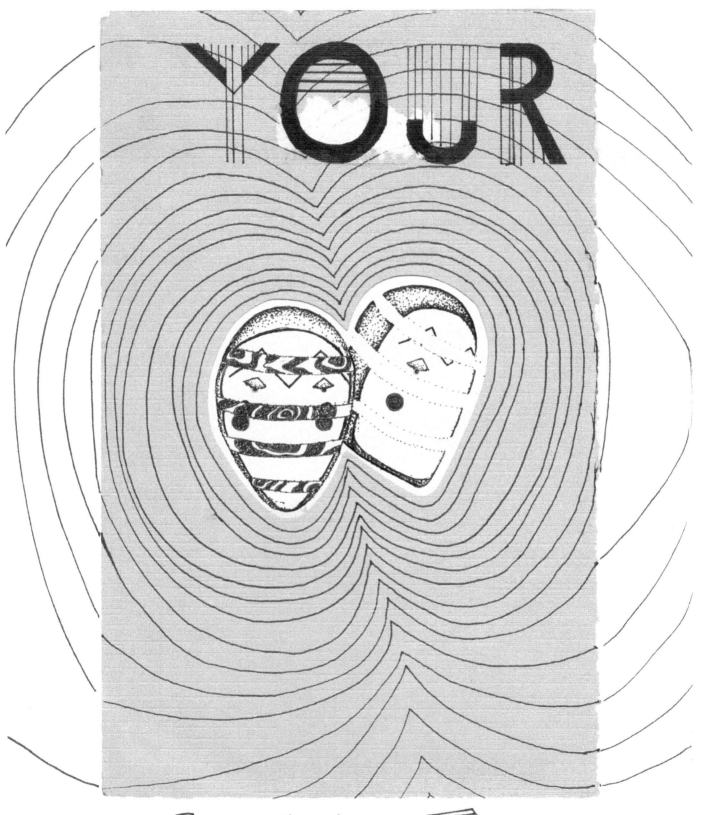

Group One

The sun is moving quickly across the sky, and she worries they are not moving as quickly. Desertia and Rio have taken the lead of the pack after watching the others fall off one-by-one to stop for food, water, and switching loads.

Crystal and Dime joined them in the lead as well, pausing their conversation about their past lives. Dime rolls the mattresses behind him with a thick rope. Both of them carry two bags each, one slung to the back, one to the front.

Desertia aches looking at them, and offers to carry something, hoping they will say no. They shake their heads no, and Crystal says, "You are so thoughtful, Desertia, but you should save your energy. You will need it when you get there. The group may decide to rest at some point, and you two should go as quickly as you can."

Rio thanks Crystal for her consideration, but rejects the offer to leave them behind. He will not abandon them. Desertia feels ashamed again, having already accepted the offer mentally, ready to leave them behind.

They stop to look back at the group, everyone still visible in the distance but getting smaller as the four of them keep pushing forward. Rio suggests they wait for a moment for the few walking to catch up so they can discuss a game plan. Desertia moves to the trees for meditation while they wait.

Crystal and Dime set their loads down and lay in the shade, and Rio digs in his bag for a snack.

As Desertia sits with her eyes closed, she cannot take the mind away from her abandoning tendencies. Whether it is seen as detachment or independence, she does not know. Regardless, the shame does not actually come from the doing, it comes from the reputation she has created for her Self in her own mind.

Desertia can understand that she was not born this way; it was a story she identified with many past lives ago, when she was a young girl. And each life experience after that was shaped by the story, "I don't need you." Again and again she attracted temporary people, sensations, places, and experiences, just so she could prove to her Self that she did not need anything outside of her for survival. A blessing and a curse.

Reg catches up, and she can hear him and Rio discussing the next steps. Reg suggests they mark their path for the remainder of the group with a certain indicator, perhaps tying clothes to cacti or stacking rocks along the way. Rio agrees and recommends there be no more than two groups.

She empathizes with his concern, beginning to worry about someone getting hurt or lost. Instead of feeling upset or making an impulsive decision, meditation allows her to sit with and observe the arising concerns and shame.

Return to your identified wound. How has this wound shaped your behavior?
What have you done, or not done, to "protect" this wound?

Journal Entry 6

Dear Moraine,

Another cycle of this life experience makes itself into the past and present, but it can no longer be my future.

I've been being the "other" girl, the one who wants to be loved first, but comes second. The girl that boys cheat on their partners with and obsesses over boys that say "If I had time," but never create it.

Was I just looking for someone to put me before what they already have or aspire, someone to make me feel worthy? Did I let my selfish ego get in the way if I knew I didn't actually want to commit?

Am I currently committing to saving the day with the same selfish intentions?

I work on settling down with people, places, and ideas, despite knowing of my inability to commit. Then, my hard work crumbles under the platforms of my expectations, and I am left sitting alone on my pile of concrete sorrow.

What would be the point of having detached from all the people and things in my life if I allow my Self to become attached now?

I am the roller coaster ride I hate to be a part of. Let me off before I scream! There is no ride, just like there is no problem—there is just my Self locked into a cart on top of my deconstructed reality.

I don't love until I am no longer loved, because I am scared to love for the fear of losing love.

What a life.

Today, things are shifting. And this time, it isn't temporary. Allow me to be with love, to associate my Self and attach to it.

Where in your life currently could you choose to be in love?

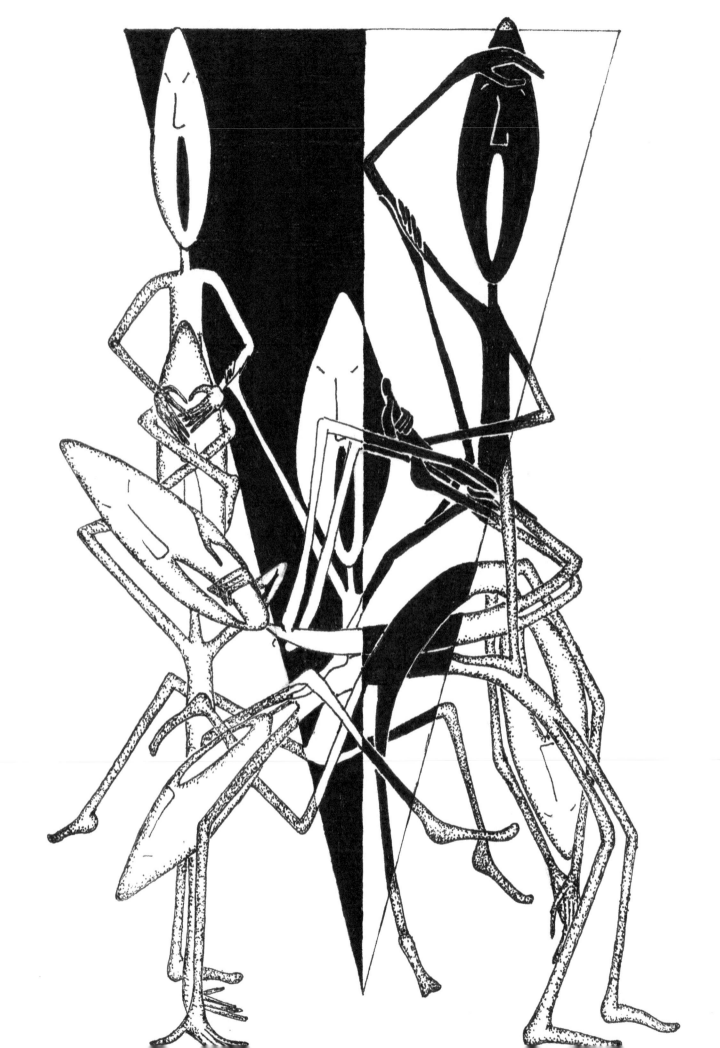

Backwards

Everyone is gathering their bags on their backs again, and she jumps up to join them. Reg has agreed to stay behind and wait for the group so he can share the plan with them.

Desertia reminds Reg the sun will be setting soon, and asks if they are prepared for their first evening in the desert.

"I think collectively the crew knows how to start a fire, and Labora has some canned ravioli for us to share," he says confidently, but his eyes speak a different language.

She can sense he is intimidated by the dark vastness, and when she glances at Rio and Crystal, she knows they can sense it too.

"Maybe we can just call it a day and set up camp, so everyone feels confident when the group splits," Rio says. Desertia notices her conditioned body wants to roll her eyes at his daddy role, but remains with the compassion and concern for the city-dwellers. Also aware of his abandonment wound, she supports his idea and begins walking back toward the group without a word.

Feelings of resentment arise, as she never walks the same path twice, but she just observes these feelings, walking mindfully and quietly amongst the group. To observe, she must refrain from identifying with the mind's thoughts, to not be upset with or excited by them, to especially become aware of the verdicts passed on her initial judgments.

Reg shares a "camping trip to hell" story, when he drunkenly fell into the campfire and woke up in the middle of the forest without light or knowing where his friends were.

"When I woke up the next morning, I was covered in blood, and we couldn't identify where it was coming from," he says, cracking up at the memory.

Desertia is reminded again of her only option to trust a stranger's word. Why resist? She laughs quietly, putting her Self in his shoes for the experience. The fear that captured him in those moments, now diminished by comedy in memory. Everything, good or bad, is temporary.

When they meet the crew, Desertia feels she made the right decision to reconnect with everyone. Some are exhausted, some are just going with the flow of conversation, pulling over if their listening ears need a break. Hauns lets everyone in on his insecurities about being out of shape, but is reassured when many others relate.

The sun is setting now, and a plan is created to separate groups the next morning, divide and reallocate luggage so Crystal, Dime, Reg, and Hauns can keep up with Rio and Desertia. They will leave a trail for them to follow, and at worst case, they can travel west until they hit the road that travels from north to south, following signs from Phoenix to the Grand Canyon. She prepares for sunset, while the others prepare a fire.

Let the mind wander…
When you catch the thoughts running through your head, can you let them go just as easy?

95

Escape

Desertia does not get up to join them for dinner, she does not feel like she is missing out when she hears their laughter at jokes and their silly games. Instead, she is focused. It has only been two days since her last meditation, and she easily falls back into it like a New York City bartender who is sleeping for the first time in 48 hours.

Meditation can feel like a drug for her sometimes, an addiction to escape. With everything, however, Desertia trusts that the cyclic cravings she goes through are not only temporary, but necessary. She believed this when she would crave meat as a vegetarian or cigarettes after a long break from smoking. Maybe the body needs more substantial energy, so it craves meat, or perhaps the mind needs a break from deep dives into complex concepts, so it craves the mindless task of smoking.

Today, her soul needs alone time, to hide away from stimulations, a moment to reflect on what's actually going on, rather than the reality perceived impulsively by the mind. In this space, alone and quiet, she is connected with the Self, here she is the most powerful as a healer and a friend.

After the crew quiets down, trailing off one at a time to the mattresses littered across the desert floor, Desertia allows her Self to rest from focusing, giving the mind its freedom to wander, all the while observing where it takes her.

The sky is filled with dark clouds, but she is not sure if they are saturated with rain or dark from the night. A ladder appears in front of her, and she grabs a hold of the bar at eye level, pulling herself up into the clouds. As she climbs, Desertia can see through the bottom of the transparent clouds above her. Two sets of feet stand on the first layer; before she can even hesitate to meet the strangers, she is lifting her right foot over the final step, placing it onto the cloud.

Two naked humans look down at her, their faces not surprised to see her.

"You made it!" one shouts. The other claps their hands as they run toward her. She steps back in shock, slipping backward off the cloud, but they grab her hands and pull her forward. Crashing onto her knees, she sinks into the cloud's fluff, like quicksand, until her feet poke out the bottom and her arms struggle to hold her on the surface level.

The strangers approach her, kneeling down by each of her arms. She sees their androgynous faces clearly now, beautiful light and dark skin colors, high and tight cheekbones, and compassionate, worried eyes.

"You can escape at any time," the same one who spoke before says, "You just have to lift your arms so you can slip through this darkness."

Her arms lift involuntarily, and her chest and head sink through the layer, until the body is falling swiftly back awake.

You can escape at anytime...
What are you clinging onto?

96

Urgency

Desertia watches the body fall horizontally from the clouds in the sky, limp, weightless against gravity's pull. As the body nears the ground, her anxiety builds as she awaits the sound of her crashing to earth, either a loud smack or an explosion of sorts. Instead, the body becomes transparent like the clouds, fading more the closer it gets to Earth's floor, never actually touching it before she is absorbed by the darkness.

She returns her attention to her cross-legged body sitting in silence on the desert floor. She has been aware the whole time, aware she was not dreaming. The mind was only wandering as she let it, her Self observing without judgment, without question.

Now, the mind is the one questioning "Who, what, why?" These strangers were so specific, their excitement to see her so honest, the location of their meeting so unusual. And why? Desertia wants to attach a meaning, discover an answer for her Self. Instead, she accepts it for what it is—unclear. The answers only ever reveal themselves when she is not seeking them.

The moon is setting faster than usual, she thinks, and the sun is approaching on the east behind a sleepy family. As the light transcends the darkness, she can see Rio sitting by the fire pit, kicking dust around as the sun comes up slowly. She can sense he is feeling stressed, perhaps rushed, and she wishes they could continue alone.

She stands on the cool desert floor, stretching her arms and legs as far as they can extend in opposite directions. When she lets go of the stretch, the body rushes with blood from her head to her toes, an ecstatic sensation she loves starting the day with.

Rio notices her approaching and meets her quickly, panicked. "Desertia, we need to get moving. I had a terrible vivid dream this morning about my son drowning in the river, because I was not there to save him. I know the elder is calling me back."

Instead of responding in words, she just moves to the bed Crystal and Dime are snuggled on top of under some blankets. They look like love, Crystal's hand resting gently on Dimes cheek, her forehead tucked under his nose. She could watch any human sleep for hours, but she knows she cannot waste anymore time.

Kneeling down, she runs her fingers through Crystal's hair, careful to wake her soothingly, so not to scare her first thing in the morning. Crystal resists it at first, but Dime wakes up from the movement in front of his closed eyelids. "Is it time to go?" he says half asleep, rolling onto his back and rubbing his eyes. Crystal stirs now.

When Crystal opens her eyes and see's Desertia, she rests her hand on Desertia's cheek and says, "You two go. We will meet you there with our family."

She suddenly sees her Self between families, a straggler, and wonders how she ended up alone again. Speechless, she parts from Crystal, and Rio follows her into the dusk.

What questions do you seek answers to?
Are you willing to leave them in the unknown?

Part 3

Gone

Desertia remembers the moment she manifested them alone on their journey, when she saw him stressed in the rising sun and wished they could continue without the group. She reflects on what her intentions were. Why does she want to be alone with him? Or does she just want to be without everyone else?

They walk in silence for most of the day, and she falls behind him when the silence becomes too intense. Is he processing his dream? Does he feel regret for wasting time? Desertia is uncertain, but she tries to understand the tension until she cannot bear the weight any longer.

Despite their moving at a pace to which she is unaccustomed, and surprised he is able to move so efficiently with the amount of luggage he carries, she remains mindful, leaving directions for the crew to follow. When she falls behind Rio, she watches the arch and bend of her feet, the way her toes spread to grab the Earth with each step. She feels the rocks, the sand, and occasionally the cactus thorn.

The landscape is transforming constantly, from light green cacti forests and yellow desert sand to red-orange mountains giving life to lush, dark green juniper and pine forests. Her inner compass guides her through the trees, and he is always one step ahead of her having walked this path many times. Occasionally they even cross old tracks and, based on his movement in their direction, she assumes they are his.

The noon sun blazes over them just as they merge with the trees, and she is grateful for the protection of her rooted guardians. Now, the sun is beginning its early afternoon descent, and they have yet to take a break for rest. She feels strong, but her feet are raw from the sand-to-pine-needle transition. Either her ego does not want to appear weak in front of this persevering man, or she feels shame in making him stop in a time of life or death.

An eagerness is also present in her, an excitement to see what has come of the national park and curiosity to explore the minds of the community. She recognizes her guard is rising at the thought of interacting with an entire community of strangers, remembering how she was so quickly disregarded from the family she felt she had just meshed with in the city.

She mentally lifts her arms to let go of the cloud she has desperately clung to for so long, the story of loneliness and unworthiness. As if the cloud is her truest reality, she can feel her Self fall through the cool, wet air and into the warm embrace of a new family, or at least a new concept of the word.

Letting go of her ego's concerns, the "what ifs" of honoring her vessel, she catches up with Rio to ask, "Are you planning to walk through the night?"

He gives her a cold, short "yes," never looking away from the direction he is heading.

Are you a straggler, wandering between groups, or do you prioritize the family you have cultivated?

Here

Desertia's mind starts to race in every direction, playing with the possibilities that might result from being alone with this detached human being, a stranger once again.

Are they really going to a community? Or is he leading them back to his home in the woods, where she is never to be found? Was the whole crew in on this plan? Would she have come if no one else were keen to join?

Her legs feel the constant walking, practically jogging to keep up with Rio's long strides. The momentum is putting her in an airy state, fleeting from one unmindful assumption to the next. Needing to ground, she politely asks Rio to stop for sunset so she can meditate, suggesting they continue at dark.

He reluctantly agrees, and she asks him to sit with her, feeling he may benefit from grounding as well. When he chooses a spot on the ground, she sits with crossed legs directly in front of him, staring at his darting eyes.

"I want to connect quickly. Please, give me insight into your mind," Desertia says bluntly, "What is going on up there?"

Rio sighs, unable to make eye contact with her, so out of touch with the present moment and the reality they share together. "I can't get out of my nightmare. My wife may be upset, the elder may be dying, the community may be falling apart, and I have been fooling around with city dwellers."

"You're upset, I can see it. You are rushed, I can feel it… in my legs. Did you forget where you are?" she asks with intentional gentleness.

"No, I've walked this trail many times."

"Great! I am glad you know where we are going, but I am asking if you forgot where you are. On a micro level, you are a speck of dust bonded to a ball of water and mass. You are a drop of water in the ocean. You are a human on a journey to Self, manifested as a husband, father, and community warrior on a mission. But most of all, you are here. Where is here for you?"

He gazes around at the forest before closing his eyes and sinking into his body, feeling where his burning muscles rest on the cool Earth. He stays in his observation for some time, so she grounds into her surroundings as well. She is here, sitting on the Earth's bare ground, held together by the trees and nourished by the sun. She is with Rio, the wandering soul that manifests itself in many forms to meet her over and over again.

Rio interrupts her to say, "Here is the breath, the heartbeat, the trees brushing their branches together in the wind. Here is what is a part of me now, what is with me. Even the sounds are a part of me, as they are in my listening. Where I have been all day is there, where I am not, that which I am disconnected from. I have been in my head."

Where is here for you?

104

take a
look inside your mind

don't be afraid to get lost

Spiral

Desertia takes Rio's hands, placing his open palms face down on top of hers. Watching him shift in being, a switch turns on in her, and a nurturing mother replaces her inner child; she is a healer. He is no longer detached, but present. She is no longer the curious and vulnerable, but the intuitive, wise, and strong.

With his hands in hers, she closes her eyes, grounding them into the "here" they just established for themselves. She sees roots growing from their limbs, diving deep into the ground. They must become the roots to understand where they are going. Like cells in the blood, the two souls float down the roots, riding the waves of natural growth as it extends downward, spiraling.

The ride ends at the Source. For the tree, it is water stored deep beneath the surface in natural reservoirs. For them, it is Truth, buried under seemingly endless layers of inherited illusion.

She takes them so far down the spiral she begins to doubt they are going anywhere. Debating whether to pull back or continue a little further, the roots shoot them out, and they are hurtled into a bright white light, neither moving forward nor standing on any surface. They are simply absorbed by everything and nothing.

Having tapped into the medicine, the white light and life source of all things, she moves the light into Rio's body through their palms. Their hands throb with each pulse of light until it becomes a steady flow, rushing down her spine from the crown of her head, circulating through her bloodstream and nerves.

Their bodies become one with the white light, one with each other. With eyes closed, Desertia watches his soul drift upward, departing from his vessel. She follows him up and out, where they stand observing the connected bodies, cross-legged, hand in hand, a white river of light flooding through them.

From this perspective, she can see the medicine working to heal the area around his sternum, the point of inner-security, self-worth, and self-love. Desertia can see that the reason he is rushing has less to do with his love for his community and more to do with the fear of what they may think of him if he fails. Rio's perception of worth is dependent on his family's confirmation.

She looks over at his soul, wondering if he can see the same thing. He is not looking at their bodies on the ground; he is looking at her. His eyes reveal sadness, shock, and she understands this is likely his first time seeing his Self, his first time outside the mind and body.

They look down at his shaking body, tears streaming down his face. Her work is done; his has just begun. He understands what has been taking him away from "here." They open their eyes, now sitting back in their vessels, his dammed emotions pouring out.

What do you love to do?
Can you identify the underlying intentions—what are you trying to achieve?

Soul Tie

Rio rubs his eyes, embarrassed to make eye contact, vulnerable about what she just witnessed in him. Desertia does not say anything, just observes him, as if still pushing the light medicine through him with her eyes, injected with compassion.

She remembers their moment in the bedroom with Crystal, how the two of them held space for her without infringing upon her feelings with their beliefs, ideas, and concerns, without touching her with reassurance of her already valid feelings. She sets an intention for her Self to offer the same space for Rio as he reflects on what has happened and observes what is currently happening in his mind, body, and soul.

His mind identifies the emotions as sadness, experiences mental exhaustion from doing the necessary work. His body experiences short breaths getting longer, smoother, his sagging shoulders lifting, the tightness in his heart releasing as he comes back to a calm center.

Rio's soul understands the tie and pain of abandonment, spending every day just trying to prove to his Self that he is worthy of love, of someone staying for him, of success and happiness. He seeks proof in the validation of others. The soul consciously chooses to release the weight on his heart, like picking a rock off a delicate sprouting bud, so the heart can be nourished to its full potential.

This is only the beginning of the healing process—awareness. Much work remains to lift the pain, many steps to take on his journey to self-love.

With a deep sigh he says, "I realize now that you bear no gift for me, Desertia. You are the gift. The community will see in unison the ways in which they individually affect the well-being of the group.

The elder cannot heal us by himself; we must take responsibility for our own faults in destruction. He has been carrying all of our weight, it is no wonder he is sick.

I knew you were powerful from the moment I saw you barefoot and vibrant at the trading post, but I am humbled by how much I underestimated your power."

She feels uncomfortable accepting his compliment, equally surprised at her abilities to guide others in escaping reality as they know it, allowing them to see their Self from a bird's-eye-view. Although the light medicine passes through her vessel, she cannot take responsibility for the healing. Remembering her intention to remain unbiased in his discovery, she lets go of her experience.

He does not say anything more. Instead, he closes his eyes and moves inward to reflect on this journey to Self. They sit in silence together, yet on separate journeys. Behind closed eyes she notices the sun has set, and she rubs her feet, preparing to continue on their path through the night.

Think of your own faults, your destructions…
What have you yet to take responsibility for?

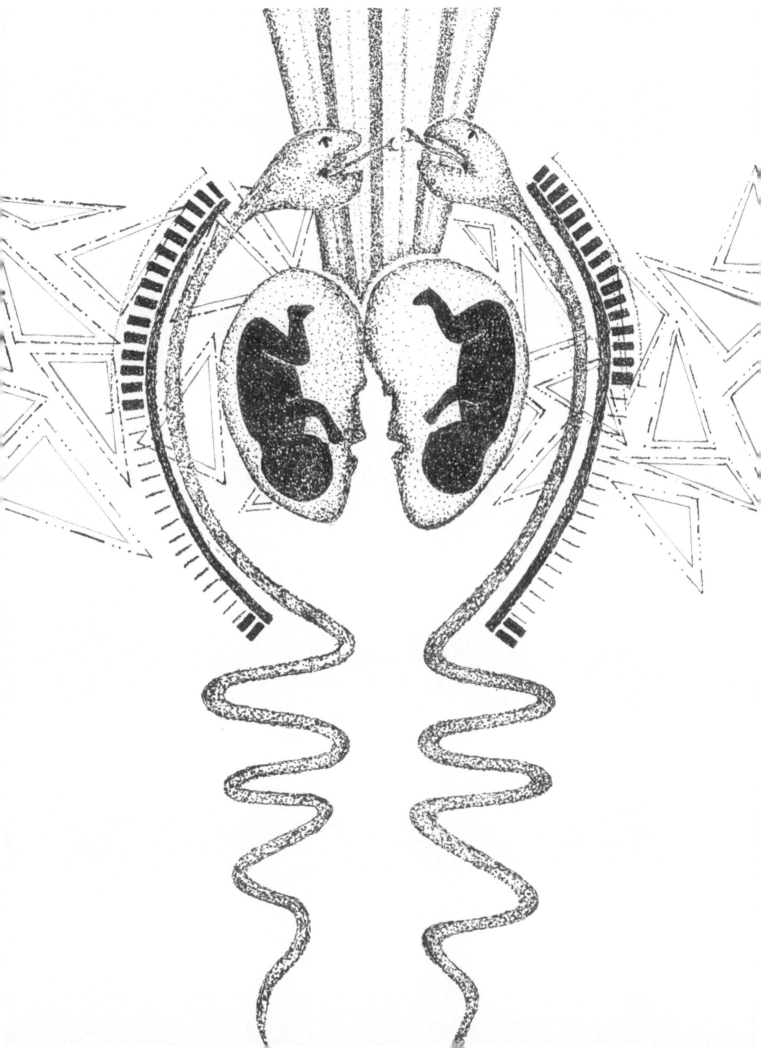

Subjective Perspective

Their footsteps are quiet in the night, this time without tension, only love. Rio grabs her hand from time to time, flashing white teeth at her with each connection. The eyes' transition to night vision always inspires her, how adaptable this part of the vessel can be, a valuable tool that relates most creatures.

Desertia enjoys the calmness, the subtle sounds of their feet stepping over pine needles, the cool, soft wind blowing through the trees. His warm hands contrast with the cold, his bright smile contrasts with the dark.

This time, when he grabs her hands, he stops walking and holds her hands to his chest. She does not feel scared or intimidated by this man in the dark, and she gazes up at him with curiosity.

"We will reach the park at any moment, Desertia, and then we must descend into the canyon. I want to check in with you, how are you feeling?"

She thinks about it for a moment, realizing that she has not been thinking about what she is entering into since before their last stop. "I feel weightless, like I am floating. I know this is where I am meant to be," she concludes.

He pulls her in gently for a hug, kissing the top of her head before resting his cheek on the crown of her head. She feels like a little girl, reminded of her own ability to adapt quickly in situations that require a woman, a mother.

The sun is rising when they enter the park. Old ticket booths with shattered windows and graffiti welcome them with an eerie reminder of what once was. There were times she waited in these lines for hours, feeling stressed at the price of tickets and lack of campsites. It seemed every time she went was spontaneous, a shot in the dark; she and her friends would often have to sleep in the car at the nearest grocery store parking lot.

Now, no one. No stress. No long lines. No fees or even need for campsites. The paint on the road is worn, the overgrown trees' roots shattering the sun-stripped tar. A road that appears to carry cars off the canyon edge, straight and direct as far as the eye can see, leads them quickly to their destination.

An empty parking lot, demolished outhouses, and a vandalized visitor center are all that remain from her memories. Here, she would talk with returning rim-to-rim trailblazers about their journeys, while her friends sought direction from park rangers and trail maps.

Desertia wants to be alone, to explore what is current from her past life, and leaves Rio overlooking the canyon's rim to explore the visitor center. She wanders over to the shattered glass cases, once housing beautifully crafted baskets, clothes, and jewelry from ancestors that used to live in this area.

She has always been disturbed by the chaos white settlers caused the Native Americans.

The road on her travels around the States always led her to cultural museums, admiring the artistries of the nomadic people and their trade economies.

If she is the creator of this Life, was romanticizing native history an unconscious manifestation of the pandemic? Was she unaware of this wish to see society catapulted back in time before technology or the dollar ruled the world?

Her mind is spinning in circles, crashing into and over itself, as she ponders this idea. The real question would be then, if she has that much power over the collective experience, does Life begin and end with her? Did the Natives manifest their own decimation or did she?

In an attempt to calm the philosophical mind, she remembers that these types of questions may never reveal concrete answers, so best not to become dizzied by them.

She understands that no one is right or wrong in the evolution of humanity, everyone is just doing what they think is right, most often avoiding what they consider to be wrong. Yet, each circumstance is subjective.

Rio shouts for her through the empty corridor. As she observes the floor to avoid stepping on glass fragments, she sees a string of beads peeking out under one of the cases. Discovering leads to uncovering, and she reels out a necklace, beaded with seeds. At the bottom of the chain is a heavy pendant, the tip of a buffalo horn inlaid with turquoise stones.

In disbelief, she looks up at the room around her, empty aside from the disheveled casing and some museum images on the walls. Rio steps through the doorway and sees her holding the necklace. "Sweet find!" he says.

She feels like a thief with it in her hands and at the same time a protector. This is not just a sweet find, this same necklace once sat in the hands of an ancestor, an artisan, before the white man, before the dollar, before the pandemic. This necklace was someone's reality many past lives ago.

Remembering her human tendency to classify something as right or wrong, she decides to look at it as what is so. She has uncovered an artifact, a necklace, in the ruins of man. There is no saying if she is "right" to protect it or "wrong" to take it, and she trusts that Life will take it from her or leave it with her, but right now, it is in her hands.

Slipping the necklace over her head, she follows Rio to the canyon edge, where they peer into nature's greatest optical illusion. Horizontal lines fade from red to white, brown to black, shaped in waves by the ever sinking and twisting river.

Rio glances at her, "Are you ready?" She nods and they step over.

Remember a time when you were ridiculed for doing, what you thought was, the right thing.
Remember a time when you ridiculed someone for doing, what they thought was, the right thing.

Infinite

The morning is still young, inviting a cool breeze to carry them down the zigzagged canyon walls, covered by the shade as the sun rises behind the canyon. Her feet ache but are resilient with thick calluses guarding her soles.

Reminded by her jingling bells to remain mindful, Desertia falls back on occasion to appreciate the psychedelic beauty of the canyon descent. She observes the changing shapes of the thick white clouds, how they reflect darkness onto the canyon walls and floors, the temporary shade provided for her as the Sun hides, drifting behind one cloud at a time.

The farther down they glide, the farther the sun glides west, until it is directly over them. Mid-day, they reach a point to rest under some trees, a small stream trickling by, providing life to the young spruce.

Rio takes off his sweaty shirt, splashing his face and chest with water from the stream, his chest and back covered by one big tattoo, a warrior's shield. She sits by a quaking aspen, and sifts through the layers of purple, yellow, and red sand. Gathering a handful, she lets the clump disintegrate back into the larger Earth. The sand, fragments of these canyon walls, teach her the importance of surrender and letting go.

Thinking back to her goodbye with Crystal, how she feels severed from the family, Desertia thinks of her Self as a granule of sand, the family a canyon. It does not matter how many times the wind picks her up, she will land back on the canyon floor. The cycle will continue eternally, as the walls of family are beyond her.

A family is infinitely larger than the mind wants her to believe, and she will continue to merge with and separate from the connections she makes along her journey. Observing Rio taking off his shoes by the water, she feels a sadness come over her. One day she will part from him, too.

"Desertia, come lay in this water! It feels great," he calls to her, when he notices she is watching him.

She has always thought of her Self as a cat, not particularly enjoying the thought of being in water. A flashback to a nature documentary on wild lynx pops in her mind. It resonated with her when the deep narrating voice said, "You will only see the same lynx once, as they are constantly migrating."

Rio splashes a small handful of water in her direction and she shrieks playfully, giving in. This may be the last time she ever sees Rio alone, the most authentic reflection of his Self she can obtain. She walks over to the water, pretending she cannot feel him watching her as she strips down to her bare skin, the most authentic reflection of her Self.

Where has the wind picked you up and dropped you?
Who have you called "family" that you now know to be a stranger?

113

Attraction

The water comes up mid-shin, and when Desertia sits down, it barely reaches her hips. The combination of dry, hot air, the sun shining on her back, the icy water on her thighs makes her feel balanced. None is unbearable.

Rio sits across from her, glancing to the sky, pretending to be interested in something other than her. She is not uncomfortable being naked with him miles away from the community, his wife and child. Wondering if anyone uses swimsuits these days, she observes Rio's defined arms and lifted chest. She is very attracted to him but, with her mindful practices, does not fall into the lust she once had with unavailable men.

The way Desertia admires people has changed considerably since being on her own. She is attracted to everyone, since she sees so few people, and must be intentional and clear on what it is that attracts her. She is attracted to the softness beneath Rio's rebellion and detachment, a mask disguising his dictated consideration for others. She appreciates his versatility.

"Why are you looking at me like that?" he asks blushing.

She blushes too, forgetting that she was staring at him while the mind wandered, only able to imagine what look she may have been directing at his body. "My mind drifted, I didn't give you any intentional look," she responds.

"Tell me, where does your mind go when you look at me?"

She can sense where the conversation is heading, how he seeks affirmation and compliments. He wants to feel loved, seen in his naked glory. Perhaps he even wants to see her bare, to touch her, kiss her. It has been a long time since she has been intimate with any person, yet she knows the face of desire and she is staring it in the eyes.

"Tell me where your mind is right now," she jokes, "I have a feeling I may already know the answer, but I am interested to confirm or deny." She does not want to play this game, but she knows she has been deep in it since she met him. "Do you feel attracted to me?" she asks, feeling childish in her wording.

"If you can read my mind, you tell me," he says coolly. "What is attraction anyway?"

She sits silent for a moment, thinking of a witty response that might end the game and get her an answer. "It is different for everyone, so that is for you to discover."

"I think you are beautiful. Am I attracted to you? Very. And in more ways than one. Obviously I can only live with those thoughts in my imagination, but the more time I spend with you, the more I want to be around you," he says as he steps out of the water.

Look desire in the eye...
Are the mind, body, and spirit attracted to the same thing?

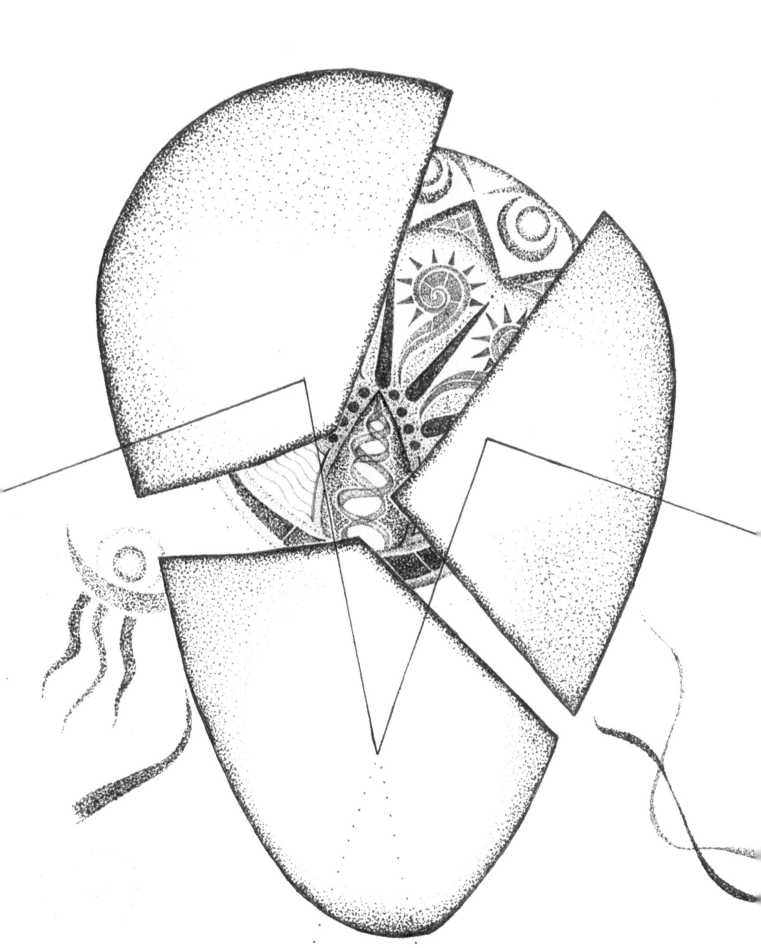

Journal Entry 7

Dear Moraine,

Are we dreaming?

In lucid dreaming, each character is merely a reflection of the subconscious. A message shared is not from the character, but from the entity of the mind—an extension of the Self.

If I can remember correctly, he said to me,

"The more time I spend with you, the more I want to be around you."

In the wake state, I perceive this as a complement.

I feel the same way about him. His mind is so intriguing, beautifully crafted with positive intentions. He influences me to be a more complete version of my Self, which is considerate, compassionate, and sacrificial.

If this is a dream, I perceive it as a reflection.

Life is a spider web of dew drops reflecting our own thoughts, perceptions + creations. If this were a dream, his words would actually be my subconscious complimenting my Self. In other words, the more time I spend with my Self, the more I desire it.

The more I focus on being here, gratitude, and creating a positive Life, the more I want to stay grounded in this perspective, empty of fear and illusion.

I thank Life for bringing me all this way to experience such a profound peace.

Life is a spider web of dew drops…
What did someone reflect back to you today?

Impressions

They are walking the final stretch to the community. The hottest hours are behind them, and Rio is confident they will make it before dark.

As if Desertia is walking onto a stage to give a speech to an entire community of people, the mind is suggesting she be nervous, the body responding with nauseating anxiety. Her soul, however, having gotten a dose of the white medicine, is not fooled and she remains separate from the sensations that wish to turn her back up the canyon wall.

Rio leads the way, pointing out spots where the community used to live, where they hosted gatherings, and where his wife birthed their son. An entire lifetime had been lived here already by him and his community, having filled the canyon with recent, yet out-of-reach experiences.

She enjoys listening to the way he tells stories, giving dramatic pauses between sentences and laughing hysterically before ever getting to the funny part. A couple of times they had to stop, and she found her Self belly laughing with him, making memories of their own.

Laughter seems to lift a veil from her way of being—rigid and closed, so thoughtful of each word. Without the veil, she expresses her Self through sarcasm and immature jokes, saying the unexpected and the uncomfortable. It is more enjoyable when the person is witnessing this layer of her for the first time.

They are laughing and reminiscing about high school. He had just moved to the States his freshman year, and his perspectives, his lens clouded by culture, were hilarious for her to hear. They considered him a "skater boy" because of his resistance to authority. She was considered a "cool girl" to the guys, thanks to yoga pants, therefore a "threat" to the girls. Rio's main theme in school was trying to navigate American women; her theme was trying to hide from them.

Just as they are diving into an explicit conversation about their first sexual experiences and sending booming laughter through the canyon, a woman appears on the trail in front of them carrying a basket filled with prickly pears. Desertia knows right away that she has overheard them based on her facial expression, disgust.

"Alana!" Rio shouts, half surprised and half excited.

"Rio! I can't believe you are back, Saba has been worried to the point of rescue."

His eyebrows raise then furrow, "Why? I have only been gone a couple days. This has been one of my shortest leaves."

"I suppose she was experiencing intuitive feelings of needing to worry," she says, raising her eyebrows at Desertia. "I am sure everyone will be pleased you brought a friend."

Each day we are faced with first impressions, starting with our Self in the bathroom mirror. How will you greet your Self today to give your best first impression? Tomorrow?

117

Community

Rio brushes off Alana's cold commentary, but what remains for Desertia is an uncomfortable feeling of entering this new community after making a bad impression. They walk past Alana, leaving her to harvest the cacti fruits, remaining silent until they are out of earshot.

"I am sorry about her, Desertia," he says, breaking the awkward silence and interrupting her spiraling thought process. "She is my wife's good friend and is just being protective."

Back to high school, she thinks to her Self, before realizing the destruction of her thoughts. Instead, she does not say anything, recreating in her mind the possibility of becoming close friends with Saba and even Alana. When they understand why she has come, they will look up to her, not down at her. Desertia will show them what lies behind their judgments—their pain. They will understand that what they see in her is merely their own projections.

Small huts begin to appear below. About fifty people are scattered between the houses. Parents talk closely while their children play. Desertia wonders if news of their arrival has already spread that quickly, reminding her Self that Alana is behind them. How loud were she and Rio laughing and shouting?

A line of men and women are carrying pails of dirt, dug out of the opposite canyon wall, towards a construction site on the far west of the camp. Elders sit outside a home smoking rolled tobacco leaves.

The closer she gets to the camp and the farther she gets away from her undesirable train of thought, the livelier and more vibrant the community becomes. They reach the ground floor, Rio shaking hands and hugging the men celebrating his return. A young child gallops toward them shrieking—his son.

Rio runs to his baby, picking him up and spinning in a circle, letting his little legs fly freely. He stops spinning and kisses the boy's head many times before setting him down on the ground.

His wife, Saba, approaches, following the young boy to his father. She has a long red cotton dress with buttons in the front, a large red scarf draped over her head and shoulders, and strappy woven sandals. Her dark brown hair and light brown eyes compliment her smooth olive skin.

"Rio," she says softly, pulling his attention away from the boy and onto her. They kiss passionately, and Desertia looks at the sky, not knowing where to divert her attention or which strangers' eyes to meet.

Saba has to push him off her, laughing as he jokingly starts kissing her neck in front of everyone. He turns and lifts an arm in Desertia's direction, "Everyone, this is Desertia, the sweet spirit who has come to assist us in healing Ramón."

Expecting a clap or any sign of gratitude, their silence and uncomfortable stares disappoint her. Feeling like she has entered a sorority initiation, a need for confidence is apparent.

Are they waiting for a speech?

Rio steps in, embarrassed by the behavior of his family members, "Have you each lost your mind while I was gone, or just your manners? Smile for Christ sake, or tell me the bad news."

"There is no bad news yet Rio, but I am sure Ramón will be eager to see her right away. He is in his room if you wish to take her," a young man in his late twenties says.

"Thank you, Sean. We will see him now," he says, taking Desertia's hand in his.

She pulls back involuntarily, giving him a frowning expression as if to say, "This is not the place for hand holding." He gives a sarcastic chuckle, overwhelmed by the hard clash of this introduction. She is grateful they did not show up with the entire city-dweller crew, manifesting he can prepare the community better for that.

They wander through the scattered homes, receiving smiles from the women, much appreciated. A crowd of children run behind them toward the elder's home. When she looks back, everyone in the camp has stopped what they are doing to watch the newcomer, the healer.

"Saba invited us to a gathering tonight to welcome us home," Rio says holding the door open for her. "I'm sure everyone will warm up by then. They do not see people from outside often, if at all."

It eases her discomfort to know there is potential for connection, a chance to shine her light and win some smiles. She stops Rio in the doorway, "Do you think our hand holding is accepted here, especially by the women?"

"Are you seeking approval?" he laughs, and she cringes. "Of course it is accepted. The community does not connect hand holding with intimacy, just connection of two beings.

It's important that you know, although I am married, as most of us are, the concept of husband and wife is simply a commitment to exclusively make children with one another in this community, to avoid incest in the future. Most of the community still takes the traditional approach to relationships, but Saba and I are what one might consider 'open.'"

She understands what he is saying, but not what he is intending by informing her. Is he referring to the handholding or to their conversation in the stream earlier? Before she can ask, a small girl in her early teens enters the living room, inviting them into the bedroom to visit the elder.

The way others make us feel is merely a reflection of the way we feel about our Self...
Do you feel welcomed or do you feel judged?

Elder

Rio suggests she enter the room alone for introduction, "He knows you are coming." Desertia agrees, walking slowly into his space to avoid disrupting or surprising him in sleep.

The elder is frail, weak, but still young, a child in his dreams. His native features—straight, long salt-and-pepper hair and flat face—complement his Latino features—a short nose and facial hair. She trips over the rug and her bells jingle loudly, alerting him someone is in the room. The body freezes and she feels embarrassed by her unawareness. His eyes open, but he cannot lift his head.

"Belle? Is that you?" he asks with a Spanish accent.

"It is me, Desertia. I am a healer and a friend of Rio's."

"Ah, yes, sister. I called to Rio in his sleep. I am very ill. The Gods showed me he was bringing you. Please, stand closer so I can see your face."

Setting the Magic Bag down, Desertia floats toward the bed. Standing directly over him, she sees the sickness manifesting in his cheeks, sagging and tinted purple from his stressed veins—a contrast with his lively eyes. He smiles, revealing some missing teeth, others quickly rotting away.

She smiles back at him, filling the space between them with a ray of white light, as if shining a flashlight on him to see through his shadows and locate the source of his dis-ease. He closes his eyes to enter this blissful sensation, and she understands that he is a healer too, good friends with the light medicine.

"I am so glad you arrived when you did," he starts, pausing for a cough, "my light has dimmed and I can no longer heal my Self. Let us go right into it, I would like to introduce my Self only when I am complete."

She can feel the light tapping at the door, ready to pour into this man, as if she had been carrying it for him and this moment all along. Without hesitation, Desertia kneels by his bed and takes his left hand to her heart, placing hers on his, closing her eyes.

A vision flashes in her memory of them sitting by a fire in the night, men surrounding the fire next to her, wearing nothing but loincloths. She does not feel afraid, because she is a man too. They all have their elbows resting on knees, facing their palms to the fire, absorbing the heat, the light.

The fire shares its warmth, transcending their stresses and offenses into floating sparks of light. Like pollen or seeds in the spring, the sparks land in the dark forests of other human souls, flourishing into a wildfire, bringing light to the unseen. She and the elder are the specks of light, the seeds that plant into the mind—the healers.

Together, they burn through a village, sending even the men running in fear. They ravish the small straw structures, taking with them the weight of the world, the material and the

120

emotional baggage that anchor humans into their suffering.

The villagers stand in the distance, watching their world perish. They cry, the ground bare except for the layer of ash, and they are left with nothing, and suddenly they have everything. When the towers crumble, there is only space for a garden to grow.

Observing the men, the women, the babies, how their grief turns to celebration, she embodies a naked woman nursing a quiet and curious child, Ramón. His dark brown eyes reflect back to her the vessel she lives inside, a native woman, a mother, happy to be with her child in safety, unsure and hopeful about what is to come for her family.

She sees fire in the baby's eyes. A lingering trauma or a burning anger, she is unsure. When she peers deeper, the fire holds an image of the elder burning miserably in the flame throws of men. He is weak, disintegrating to nothing. The people surrounding him are angry, but not at him. They are angry at one another, blaming and shaming each other for savage behaviors, yet doing nothing to put out the fire.

The baby cries, communicating that he has seen it too.

She sings to him, "The ground is bare, we are here, we are aware, do not cry my dear. The doors have opened, setting us free, we will live in harmony, you and me."

He stops crying and they watch the family around her; men and women arguing about the next move, what will be best for the community. She stands up unseen, walking slowly, mindfully away from the crowd. No one has the awareness to see her go, and so she continues undisturbed, until she and her baby are in solitude on lush ground, a foundation where their garden can grow.

She re-enters the body kneeling beside the elder's bed. His eyes are still tearing, and he opens his eyes just after she does, staring blankly at the ceiling. They sit in silence for a period. Like a baby walking for the first time, excited and wobbly, he pulls his body to a seated position in the bed.

He cannot contain his laughter and joy, the youth in his eyes glowing like a child. His laughter turns to tears, and he bows his head into his palms, detoxing all the pain he carries through sobs, loosened and broken apart by the light medicine.

Without any words or gestures of comfort, she watches him, no longer needing a proper introduction, for she has seen in him what his closest friends and family never will.

Consider your towers crumbled…
What opportunity(s) does this new ground hold?

121

Returning

"It's comforting, sister, knowing that we are connected on this soul level, through our series of lives. And, at the same time, uncomfortable to see I have lived the same life over and over again, the life of storing anger," Ramón says finally, as his body falls back onto the bed in physical exhaustion.

Desertia does not nod or shake her head, just listens, careful not to let anyone's perceptions skew hers. Were she to take that as Truth—that they are two souls linked together through many lives—then she would live out the rest of her life that way, feeling a need to connect with him again here.

Because he is not the first to draw the conclusion that their two souls are connected and have lived many lives together, she struggles to find any honesty in it. It sounds more like a trendy phrase used by a reputed guru to gain people's trust, the followers repeating it, living it.

"I spent so long, so many lives, to create and keep peace; therefore, I suffered. Peace is not something tangible; it is nothing to be grasped. Peace is within, not without. And in a community of hatred there are people who have yet to discover peace within," he continues.

"These individuals, this family, is a pool of sick fish, spreading their dis-ease, their inner turmoil, like a disease through the water that flows through all of us. I was attempting to filter it, purify it. A fish trying to purify water! Can you believe it?" he chuckles sadly for a moment.

He looks at her with teary eyes, just as she imagines she looked at Rio and Crystal the day of the city departure. "So now what?" he asks, "Are we just left to be in misery?"

She knows his question is not rhetorical, not to remain unanswered. He is seeking wisdom, guidance.

"You just left misery, why are you putting your Self back in it?" she asks, pausing to let him reflect on it. "You've just discovered the people are suffering within, and you've been taking responsibility for it, making it your own suffering."

He stares at her with concentrated thought, flipping through the channels she has just opened in his mind.

She continues, "You have nothing left to do, but live peacefully. When people notice, they will want what you have. You plant the seed by being, so you can nurture it when they are ready to grow. Your gift is peace, but who can receive it if you don't show it?"

The guidance flowing through her moves them equally, like the light medicine. She can see her areas of being in her life that heal others and those which do not. She chooses to be open, not reserved, because without it, no one will ever see her gift.

Where are you taking responsibility for other's misery?

123

Unspoken

In deep thought, Ramón falls asleep. At last, the healing process has begun. Desertia lifts her body off the floor, staring over the sleeping grown man. His inner child lay softly on the surface, resting peacefully.

She picks the Magic Bag gently off the floor, careful not to jingle too loud, digging inside for Palo Santo or sage to cleanse the space and her Self. Her hand brushes the old woman's gift, and she pulls it out of the bag—the round spineless cactus. The voice in her head guides her to place it on Ramón's bedside table; she trusts it is the herbal medicine Rio requested for the elder's healing.

On the other side of the door sits Rio, head propped back against the wall, mouth open wide, a faint snore revealing his exhaustion. She wonders why he is here and not with his wife and child. She shakes his shoulder slightly.

"Are you done?" he says startled, trying to appear he was awake the whole time.

She laughs, helping him to his feet. He rubs his eyes, a vampire in the light. She feels exhausted and wants to lie down somewhere for a while, away from everyone.

"Where can I lie down for a bit?"

"We have a spare room in our house. But I want to hear how it went, did you heal him?"

Moving toward the door, she ponders the question. Did she heal him? A doctor does not heal a fractured arm, he splints it. The arm heals itself.

"This is his healing journey, not mine. He can tell you about the experience if he wishes to," she says smiling over her shoulder at him, "Now, show me my room, please."

Rio takes the lead, and she wonders if everyone stood frozen in their spots from the moment she entered the elder's home, awaiting her return. The same people stare at her, some with curiosity, some smiling; others tend to chores pretending not to care. Children run beside them, one little girl, about three-years-old, tugging at her skirt.

Through an unspoken language, exchanging large grins, she understands the little girl loves to be seen. It has been a long time since she has held a hand so small, and her inner mother is ecstatic at the rekindling. She wants to let the girl know how much she appreciates her in this moment, to let her be seen, and she does so without words.

By observing the little girl, she can see her personality shifts from outgoing to desperate, to quiet and shy, then to outgoing again. The cycle continues. She wonders about the girl's home and family, remembering the summer camps for children with depression, in need of "extra" attention. Was it the kids who needed help or was it really the parents?

Make a list of all the ways you can share love for a stranger without saying it.

Patterns

They enter Rio's house, a small earthen home built into a mound of earth on the backside. The community adopted some architecture designs for self-sustaining homes, hauling reclaimed wood, metal, and windows down the canyon walls.

His kitchen has a lush garden inside growing staple fruits, vegetables, and herbs. Saba and her child are outside playing with neighbors, so he gives her a tour of their bedroom on the east side of the building, their kitchen and bathroom in the middle, and her bedroom on the west end.

She is grateful for the invitation into such a warm home, the walls decorated with stained glass and broken bottles. The walls are a deep red clay impregnated with orange and white, as if living inside the canyon wall itself.

"Can I get you anything?" Rio asks, not remembering—or not quite understanding—her ease of life without necessities and cravings.

She smiles at him with a grateful smile, and they hold each other tight in the hallway vibrant with abundant greenery. He kisses the top of her head before watching her part ways to her bedroom, his eyes filled with lust. Like the little girl she connected with outside, he also moves through cycles, but of socializing, desiring, and detaching.

Sitting cross-legged on the thin mattress in the corner of the room, she prepares her Self for meditation. Closing her eyes, straightening her back, heightening her senses to the noises around her, and falling into a rhythm of deep breaths, she loses touch with her perceived reality.

For the first part of meditation, she is completely grounded and focused on her breath. No thoughts can penetrate the bubble of intentional awareness she is cultivating. No imagery, no internal voices. Nothing outside of her exists inside. Bliss. Ease.

No matter how often she meditates, though, she will never be a master of the practice, only a student. The mind creeps in eventually, the moment she recognizes the blissful state meditation creates. Just when she finds what she is seeking, it vanishes from her sight, escapes her grasp.

Suddenly, she is back in the corridor with Rio, hugging tightly, observing his cyclic behavior. Exploring his world without judgment, the mirrors turn and she is peering into her own cycle.

Unavailable, curious, nurturing.

She wonders if her cycle always starts with unavailable, and if his cycle always ends with detached, concluding that cycles—like Life—have no beginning or end. Her life is the product of her cycle, all her experiences shaped and skewed by this way of being.

Can you identify your cycle in three words?

Journal Entry 8

Dear Moraine,

How did you heal?

At the beginning of our journey north, Rio mentioned that each individual is unique in their intention to heal, "you choose your method."

Although I assist in healing others, with powerful light medicine and outsider insights, I am not confident in my ability to facilitate this method of healing for my Self.

I am realizing my cyclic patterns of being today, starting with a guarded, closed-off version of me. I understand it is protection, and I know it stems from my past hurts, the pain and stories I thought I had already released.

"If you can break through my walls, if I let you in, then I love you. I am curious about you, so I can nurture your passions and healing processes."

There is something so healing for me in the act of healing others, something that would be non-existent without connection, relationships. Does this imply my healing happens through connecting with others?

Sometimes, my friendships and intimate relationships are not clean, they end "poorly," yet they are rich in knowledge, gained experience.

When it comes to relationships, the one I prioritize the most is the one with my Self.

She calls me to do the things that will inspire the necessary growth within me.

I used to love catching up with traveler friends from around the world, hearing how they have evolved on their own journey. It is apparent to me now how I sabotaged my own self-healing journey. With each meeting, I informed my new friends that our connection is not "forever," so I would not be bound by their expectations or break my own promises.

Now, I am in Love. Not with anyone specifically, just surrounded by it—the intensity of connection. Connection with others, connection with Self. I am connected to Life.

I am grateful for the connections Life has provided me thus far. Guide me to nurture connection with the people who are least welcoming of it.

How do you heal?

127

Saba

Desertia opens her eyes, not remembering having fallen asleep, still cross-legged. Someone is knocking on her bedroom door softly, and she takes a deep breath to bring her fully into the body before calling them in.

The door opens and Saba enters the room, carrying a tray with two steaming mugs. Desertia sees through the doorway that the sun is setting now.

"Would you like some tea, sister?" Saba asks, setting the tray down on a flat rock that serves as a side table.

Not wanting to create any disconnect on the first impression, she accepts the offer and invites Saba to sit on the bed, adjusting the body so her back is against the north wall. Saba takes a seat against the west wall, matching Desertia's posture with crossed legs.

"Thank you so much for helping our community," she says trying to fill the silence, "we are so grateful that your and Rio's paths aligned so quickly."

Desertia holds her hands in prayer to her chest and bows her head, unsure if the compliment is genuine. Remembering her role in creation, she chooses to manifest relationships of authenticity.

"Rio tells me you healed Ramón already."

Irritation bubbles up at the delusional fantasy Rio lives in about her healing abilities, worried that he might paint an inaccurate picture of her to the community, anxious that she might let them down under such high expectations. She sees him in her Self, seeking validation from community.

"I have started the healing process with him, yes. Only he can do the work that remains," Desertia says with a smile, to avoid coming off as defensive or condescending.

Saba sips her tea, "That is lovely. Are you coming to the gathering tonight? We are celebrating Rio's return home with music and dance."

Desertia closes her eyes to check in with the body, which now feels well rested and complete. Opening her eyes, she implies yes with a nod. She is aware that she is being unavailable and that her curiosity regarding Saba is rising; soon the cycle will complete and she will be nurturing this distant woman.

"Thank you for the invitation, I would love to join you."

"Great!" she exclaims, perking up at the idea of celebrating together, "Rio says you do not carry much, would you like to borrow some clothes for the evening?"

Another sister. Another celebration. Another outfit. The cyclic patterns of Life.

Sometimes it is easier to notice another's cycles than your own.
How are other's cycles reflecting back to you yours?

Rebirth

It is admirable to Desertia, the sisterhood that develops through the sharing of beautification. She sits on a small stool, while Saba brushes her cheeks with a homemade blush made from the light pink clay from the canyon walls.

Saba has dressed her in a clean black skirt with red and pink floral design, and a black strapless top to allow her new necklace to stand out. She offers Desertia shoes, and she politely declines, opening up to Saba about the ritual of grounding.

Saba strips down bare in front of Desertia before covering her body with a bright red fitted dress that falls below the knees. Her movements are graceful, her eyes big and round, and Desertia is surprised to discover she feels no jealousy toward this beautiful woman, only a deep relatedness and excitement to know her deeper.

The night arrives quickly, and Desertia travels with Saba and her child, Wyla, through the dark, her bells jingling softly. A bonfire in the distance is roaring high into the night sky, illuminating their path as they get closer. The drums speak deeply, summoning them down the trail.

Saba is telling the story about how she and Rio met, and how they shared a collective vision to develop this community with Ramón and the other founders. She met Rio in the city through Rio's mother, who connected them when she got sick. "Take care of one another, so humanity can live on," Rio's mother said to them on her deathbed.

She describes their love as a commitment and companionship, rather than one of romance, what she had assumed love would be as a child. When they met Ramón at a gathering in the mountains, the idea for community in this canyon was born, and they created a board to determine how they would protect one another and preserve humanity. Immediately, they conceived Wyla. Saba says pridefully, "He is the first born of the rebirth."

Desertia feels the weight of "carrying on humanity" on top of Wyla's shoulders, as well as Saba's, Rio's and the whole community. When she looks back at her journey, there have not been young children along the way, the youngest being the boy in the canyon with his father. She assumes he was ten years old.

They are approaching the celebration now, and she sees Rio shirtless, tending the fire. His muscles are swollen, his body dripping in sweat from the raging flames. Her attraction for him is expanding now that the concept of monogamy is not contradicting her feelings.

Somehow, knowing Saba and Rio's love is for humanity, not particularly one another, allows Desertia to be present with her desires, rather than resist them. A stranger to the idea of romance, she restricts her Self from engaging with him until she discovers the roots of her lust and attraction—her soul's intentions and their souls' intentions.

Who do you love?
What do you truly love about them—what are you committed to?

Reunion

Saba parts ways to surround herself with other mothers and children of the community. Adults of varying ages dance ecstatically near the music. Wind and string instruments accompany and complement the drummers, creating a high-energy tempo that seems to capture the excitement of and gratitude for Rio's return. Elders sit around the fire smoking homegrown tobacco and drinking tea.

Desertia walks slowly, observing the different groups of people, unsure where to move next. She does not want to approach Rio, but she likes the idea of sitting by the fire with the elders, not feeling in the mood to dance or talk, only observe without judgment.

Memories of parties she attended alone at University resurface. The largest university at the time, educating 80,000 students, won her tuition. Her heart sinks when she realizes most of these people have likely died by now, but her curiosity wonders who has not.

Eighty thousand students meant meeting multiple strangers every single day, and she wanted to learn each of their stories, their life journeys. Not knowing anyone and not one to participate in formal organizations, she started attending parties by herself. She would put on a costume, a name, and an accent, take a shot of whatever she could get her hands on, and walk into a stranger's home with the confidence of an invitation.

Desertia's communication skills allowed her to connect with anyone about anything until she got too drunk. She always found drinking to result in isolation, a lonely stumbling walk home. Now, she stands alone again at a party, feeling totally disconnected, and she wishes she had a child to connect her with the community mothers or that she smoked tobacco to connect with the elders.

The only person she feels connected to is Rio, and yet there is a huge barrier between them, as she attempts to understand her expectations of their co-existing.

Lost in her insecurities, Desertia does not see the stirring of the mothers and children as another group, uninvited, appears from the darkness. She hears someone shout, "Rio! Do you know these people?" and she turns her head to see who they are.

The city-dweller crew is arriving, dragging their heavy loads of belongings behind them. She spots Crystal, who looks confident in her stance, sure that she was invited here.

Rio shouts back, "They are humans, are they not?"

Before anyone can say another word, Desertia blurts, "They are family!" and runs over to greet them, crashing into Crystal's open arms, Labora shrieking with excitement. The whole crew piles on top of the girls in a group hug, and she feels grounded beneath the weight of their bodies.

For the first time, she is grateful for the weight on her shoulders. The hug offers connection, feeling of belonging, and comfort in unity.

One by one, the crew breaks away from the reunion and she looks back at the community. For the first time since her arrival, every member is smiling in her direction.

Rio joins the crew, sharing himself with the guys through hugs, while Saba approaches the new group with other women, introducing themselves and offering tea. The men sharing tobacco.

Desertia watches as Crystal and Saba fall into conversation naturally, and she feels envious that the city dwellers are receiving so much care and attention, experiencing immediate connectedness. No one will believe her first impression.

Realizing that she is the source of her own isolation, standing apart and comparing two very different encounters, she joins the women in discussion about the crew's journey.

Roxy is sharing an encounter with the still-domestic elk above the canyon, how she nearly pet the cow as it sniffed her extended hand for food. Some of the guys join the elders around the fire smoking tobacco, while the other friends from the city dance around the drum circle.

She is half listening to Crystal and Saba's conversation about the community, the same story Saba had given her earlier, and half admiring the growing community around her.

The blend of city and desert dwellers reflects back to her the coming-together of her isolation and inclusiveness. Her city family is outgoing, extending themselves to new people with ease. The desert community takes time to break through their own reserves, open but timid. City dwellers live as individuals, desert dwellers as one unit.

Desertia recognizes her Self in both of them, a scale that tips back and forth, never fully coming to equilibrium. She wonders why it often tips in the opposite direction, like gravity pulling her back from what she wants, leaving her with what she needs.

Tonight, she is getting a dose of comparison and connection, the perfect medicine to help her transcend the individual and become one with the group.

Where do you take pride in being unique?
Has this quality ever left you feeling isolated?

Dancer

Desertia watches everyone dance, their soul expression, absorbing their every move and feeling it run through the body, causing her muscles to twitch. She has always been connected to movement, exploring the different ways the body can wiggle and bend, feelings of ecstasy each time she bursts past her breaking point.

The elders are watching the dancers, some watching the drummers. She finds it fascinating how people often choose one mode of art over the other. "I can't dance" or "I am not a musician" they say, and the body is the only one listening, so it represses.

Her desire to dance is building, rising with the energy of the expanding community. As she uses a need to rest as a justification for this continuous isolation, she hears the bells on the Magic Bag jingle. Odd, she thinks, since she has not moved and the wind is mild.

Peeking over her shoulder, Desertia finds Rio standing behind her, looking around curiously, pretending as though someone other than him jingled the bells.

"Do you happen to have the rock you let me play with at the trading post?" he asks.

She smiles, once worried he would never ask. The rock weighs down the bottom of the bag, easy to locate, and she tosses it to him. He begins juggling, showing off his best tricks. Nobody can see him in the dark, and she urges him to move into the light, where he can receive the acknowledgement he deserves.

"You are the bright one, sweet spirit. Come play with me."

Something about that nickname melts her, warms her up inside, and she cannot resist his invitation. Remembering how connection is the best medicine on her healing journey, she pulls out silk fabric with silver coins lining it.

The duo steps into the light, eyes immediately focusing in on them. Desertia ties the fabric around her waist. She isolates her waist, keeping her shoulders and chest frozen, the body waving with each beat of the drum. Rio juggles behind his back and tosses the rock high in the air, completing a flip before it comes back down into his palm. They freeze and move in sync, letting the music control the show. The family cheers.

The coins clink, reminding her to be mindful of her audience, the most entertaining part of the show. Everyone, including the youngest child and oldest elder, are grinning from ear to ear, the hollering and clapping echoing off the canyon walls. Together they bow.

A scrawny old man approaches Desertia, walking with a hunch in his back. "Miss, Ramón would like to see you now. Will you follow me?"

She is excited by the invite, appreciating being sought out, specifically by the community peacemaker. Nodding, she follows him into the dark, the drum beats fading behind her.

What is your souls most potent expression?

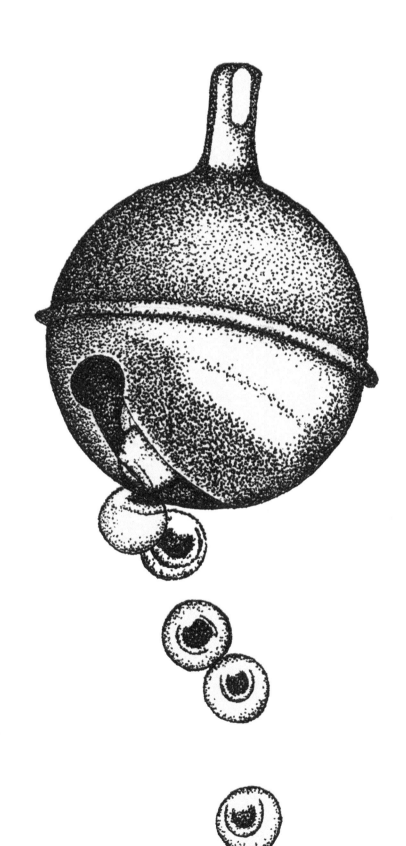

Grandfather Peyote

The smell of campfire smoke rises in the distance, and Desertia sees a flicker of light ahead. Silence accompanies her and the old man on their walk across the canyon floor and as they near the opposing wall, a rattle echoes back to her.

She freezes, remembering the snake omens and grey hair goddess. Her heart stops as her eyes peer through the dark haze. The man continues walking through the scattered shrubs, unaware of her having frozen.

Rattling echoes again, then once more, before falling into a rhythm. Desertia understands it is the elder playing a shaker. Sighing with relief, and feeling embarrassed, she runs to catch up with her guide, her bells jingling loudly, reminding her to release her insecurities.

Together, they cross the small river before approaching the south side of the fire, Ramón just barely visible through the flames, backed by the canyon wall. Next to the fire is a small dome, covered in tarps and blankets, a man-made cave.

"Thank you, Diga. Sister, please join me." Ramón summons her around the fire.

Desertia takes a seat to his right, while the old man, Diga, tends to the flames. She looks at Ramón, who appears well, sitting cross-legged, eyes closed in meditation, a brown leather sachet hanging from his neck.

Waiting patiently for him to clue her in on what is going on, she spots the cactus she gifted him earlier in his left palm. His hands are large, making the cacti look much smaller then she knew it to be. Ramón opens his eyes slowly, staring into the fire.

"I am grateful for you, sister," he says in a deep voice, "you have brought me back to my feet. You left me a gift that was given to you, and I know why. Do you?"

She hesitates, recalling the voices in her head that suggested she leave the cactus for him, assuming it was for his own healing. "Rio mentioned an herbalist, and this is the only plant I carry. It may help you on your journey," she answers.

"Ah, I acknowledge your generosity, but this gift may only help you on your journey. Do you wish to meet with Grandfather Peyote?"

The last time she heard about Peyote was in a TV series exploring plant and chemical psychedelics around the world, but she does not understand what tonight's meeting entails. Not wanting to sound foolish for not understanding what the cactus was, but not sure why she needs to meet with it, she accepts humility.

"Brother, can you tell me what good Grandfather Peyote can do for me?"

"Only you can know, my dear."

Ramón advises Desertia to ask the question to her Self, to go inward and openly receive the messages coming through. She closes her eyes, feeling the heat from the campfire light up her face. Inside, it is dark, empty, but she waits patiently for the voices or visuals to appear.

When nothing comes, she begins to worry she is wasting Ramón's time, that she is wasting Grandfather Peyote's time. Perhaps the silence implies she is meant to receive nothing. But then why bring her here, through the dark, to reunite with the gift of a dead woman?

Reflecting on her time with the grey hair goddess, her attempt to save a life, Desertia begins to observe the connection between the elements of the story. She wanted to be a healer in that moment, to free the native woman from suffering. The snake, an omen for transformation, death and rebirth, and balance of masculinity and femininity. The gift, a peyote button, a key to a new dimension of awareness.

Desertia opens her eyes, the elder looking at her with a blank stare, she wonders if Ramón's soul is still with her, or if he has already taken the medicine himself. "Brother, I'd like to set an intention for my manifestation."

"Is your intention from intuition or manifestation? They are not equal," he responds, eyes still blank.

"I am unclear of the difference," she admits.

"To manifest is to create, to intuitively feel is to know."

She ponders the riddle for a moment, asking her Self if connecting the pieces was the soul's intuition or the mind's manifestation.

"You were meant to receive, to experience a deep knowing, not to assume and create one. What good can Grandfather Peyote do for you?" he asks, staring through her.

The second time she closes her eyes to discover the answer, she sees a group of young children playing tag in a meadow, the sun shining on them, laughter filling their souls. One of them is her, but she cannot figure out which one, she can only recognize her sister.

As the young group is playing tag, she realizes she is none of them, but another child observing. Desertia wants to play, so she asks her sister if she can join. Her sister tells her to play elsewhere, to find her own friends. Looking around, she realizes the other children are her childhood friends, not her sister's, but they do not invite her to stay.

She opens her watering eyes and Ramón is with her again, staring at her not through her. He sees her tears and congratulates her on knowing.

Peyote is just another key to the locked doors of consciousness.
What can Grandfather Peyote unlock for you?

137

Sweat

"You are ready," Ramón declares, placing the cacti into a large stone mortar and pestle. He takes the leather medicine bag from around his neck and sprinkles some powder into the mortar as well. Desertia does not ask what it is, just trusts the healer's knowledge.

As he smashes it down to a paste, adding trace amounts of liquid for ease in the transformation, he chants.

"I give back to the Mother, offer her to my sister, so we can dance back to Self, back to knowing wholeness." Ramón repeats this five times slowly, until the medicine is ready.

"Sister, I offer this gift to you in gratitude for your gift this morning, allowing me to let go of what I was carrying with me all this time.

I pray to the Grandfather that you recover from blindness, so you can clearly see what's held you up on your journey. May you let go of illusion, suffering, and isolation."

Desertia feels a flash of heat travel to her head, feeling vulnerable in her transparency with him. With her hands in prayer at her heart, she bows her forehead to touch them, receiving the medicine from his large hand.

Staring at the solution, she feels a nervous disgust. She can smell the natural components of it, bitter soil. Earth.

Cacti are grounded, resilient, and protective. Desertia understands that she is coming to be one with the cacti medicine now, to be grounded, resilient, protective and protected. With that, she spoons the contents of the bowl into her mouth, head cocked back so to let it fall directly down her throat.

The taste is astringent, and the body gags at first, refusing the mixture. She forcefully holds it in her mouth until the body is ready to accept it. The medicine seeps into her gums, providing direct access to the bloodstream, and she holds the mixture to the roof of her mouth, inhaling through her nose so as not to taste. Her mind wanders, distracting her Self from the saliva building up, not wanting to purge immediately.

The body accepts it little by little, and she swallows more each time her mouth refills with saliva, until it is complete. Ramón hands her a glass of tea to wash it down quicker, then he begins chanting again, three times.

"Grandfather, Grandfather, take us home to Mother. Let your light shine the way, may she open her place and let us stay."

He stands silently, throwing tobacco into the fire, then turns toward the dome. He lifts the blankets over the door before kneeling. He bows, forehead gently tapping the earth, before crawling inside.

Ramón starts on the left side of the entrance, and moves on all fours around the pit in the middle, finishing on the right side of the door. He waves her in.

Desertia slips off the Magic Bag, remembering the necklace she discovered as it catches on the shoulder strap. She repeats his process with a bow, then enters the dome on the left side, moving clockwise until he asks her to stop directly across from him and the door.

Diga hands Ramón a large bucket of water, his rattle and drum. Ramón announces they will begin their sweat lodge now, laying down the rules. Five rounds of hot stones will be added to the lodge, four songs will be sung each round. Should she need to get out at any moment, she must ask him for the door.

"If it gets too hot, the ground is the coolest place. Do not worry if you find your body in the fetal position, face directed away from the center."

There are no words for her to say, no expectations, only a rising sensation of nausea and a heavy weight of emotions accompany the medicine. She prefers taking psychedelics with a smile and lightness, but assumes it would be disrespectful to Grandfather Peyote and the Self to be anything other than she is now.

Diga slides in six large stones balanced on a pitchfork, and Ramón uses elk antlers to place them in the pit. Diga then folds the blankets over the door, so the two sit in darkness, the only light coming from the rocks. Ramón says a prayer under his breath before scattering herbs and pouring the bucket over the fiery stones.

She can hear the scream of water hitting fire, and steam boils off the pit into her mouth, nose, and eyes. The steam burns to inhale, like cutting chili peppers, and she cannot find a pure space to breathe in oxygen. The body adapts, as if it has been here before, inhaling the smoke through clenched teeth, holding it in the mouth until it cools before releasing it again.

The body immediately begins to sweat, soaking Desertia within seconds. Her hair sticks to her face and back, and she struggles to wrap it on top of her head.

It seems impossible for her to relax, and when Ramón begins pounding on the drums, her nausea becomes overwhelming. All her attention focusing on how she will ask for the door—when can she escape?

After four medicine songs, he asks Diga to lift the blankets off the entrance. Light peers through, and she sees the body covered in slimy sand, the fresh air swooping through the door and into her deprived lungs.

Diga passes in two more stones, and the process repeats itself. The second round is more nauseating than the first. The loud drum and chanting pull out anger and discomfort—or is the anger the source of discomfort, she wonders. When the door swings open again, she shyly asks the elder to be released, aware of the saliva filling her mouth.

Identify your thresholds? Pain, pleasure, etc.
When is it too much?

139

Isolation

"Come back when you are ready," Diga says, "and take your time."

The men are so gentle with her, so accepting of her process, yet she questions if she is doing this wrong. Desertia wanders into the dark, until she can hear the river, which sings to her sweetly.

The moon lights up the sky, reflecting on the water's surface, and she sits in the cool desert-night breeze. Watching the river flow swiftly and with so much life, she can now sense the medicine has kicked in. Grandfather is here.

Her attention to detail is immaculate, seeing microcosmic structures of every plant, rock, and drop of water. The river moves in patterns, and when she follows a wave from left to right, she can hear the river singing as it washes by.

Desertia remembers the sweat lodge is happening, and feels a hesitancy to return. She feels hatred toward it. The song, the drum, the hot steam threatening the Life source. Most of all, she is in judgment of the melancholy associated with the Grandfather medicine, in judgment of her connection—or disconnect—with the experience.

As the sweat dries on the body, she feels cold. The nausea has gone with the waves, and she feels comforted by the expansion of the river. She decides to return to the campfire while Ramón finishes his sweat lodge, but as she sits there, the mind lost in the flames, she hears a lifted energy in the music coming from Diga and Ramón inside the dome.

Their songs are now exciting, their chants less serious, more joyful, and she longs to be inside the lodge. She patiently waits for the round to finish, then they invite her back in.

Two stones pile on, herbs are sprinkled over, water splashes, and she returns to the slow breath between clenched teeth. Ramón's chanting is much more vibrant now, and she feels into the drum, her shoulders jumping up and down, her upper body waving like a trained cobra.

Desertia even finds her Self chanting with Ramón. He hands her a pipe to smoke. Without effort, she feels connected with him and the medicine, and she takes a long drag. Waves of nausea return, and she transcends them through the crown of her head.

The visuals are internal and with no choice but to close her eyes, she begins to see bright traces of colors dancing on her eyelids. As the colors wrap themselves around one another, they begin to form images.

Before the images become 3D, the door opens again, letting in the light. Next round. Rocks, water, herbs. She is back in the dark, this time hotter than ever, her dehydrated body breathes deeply, her face tingling as the blood circulation slows. Afraid she might pass out, she curls into fetal position, her face tucked into the cold space above the floor.

How do you respond to structure, routine, tradition?

Dark Mysterious Truth

Behind closed eyelids, a large insect crawls over her eyes. Its cheeks are swollen, lifted by a mischievous smile. Its spider legs are long, skinny, slightly robotic in their machinery, and they scurry quickly over her right arm, on top of her head. The plump head pops upside down in front of her eyes, and it sticks out its tongue in mania, laughing in hysterics.

Desertia is not scared, only amused, remembering the reality of the journey she is on, before falling into the trap of illusion. The insect legs peel back her imaginative eyelids, catapulting her into darkness. Everything slows. A white paper package flutters from the sky, growing larger as it approaches. It lands on nothing, black vastness, where one triangle piece lifts, followed by the next, until the paper lies flat on the ground.

A tiny seed swells, cracking open, vines spiraling upward, forming into snakes. Snakes slither over a brick wall, blooming dark purple roses as they climb. A door appears and two women come out in knee high leather black boots, wearing only leather straps and silver chains. They pin Desertia to the brick wall, and a muscular man stands in front of them, tapping a baton into one hand, a bouncer. They drag her inside, slinging her forward toward the next door.

A woman's silhouette appears before Desertia. Her hands are not hands, but pointed tips, and she invites Desertia to follow her using just her body language. As the silhouette flows like a wave through through a closed curtain, a circus unravels in front of them.

Red and white pin stripes surround her in each angle, more silhouettes of women with long, wild hair, sit above her in the beams, hula hooping with their feet. The circles move in slow motion, leaving traces of circles around them, creating images of geometric flowers in the high rises.

The woman lures her backstage, and Desertia is intrigued to follow her behind the black veil. Hesitant, she pulls the curtain back and peeks behind. A backlit masculine form in a top hat awaits her on the other side. The room is dark, unpredictable. The man is mysterious, magical. Her fear of the unknown forces her eyes open.

She is back in fetal position, the hot smoke stinging her back as Ramón pours water over the rocks, still chanting. Regret washes over her for leaving the circus so soon, and she closes her eyes with hopes to return. Nothing. The body returns to a seated position, and Ramón smiles at her, "I am eager to experience what you have seen, what you will see" he says, handing her the pipe a second time.

Taking another deep inhale of the pipe and passing it back, she reassumes the fetal position. As she lets the medicines mix, Desertia becomes aware that she is unsure what is reality. Was she just imagining a sweat lodge? The story of a healer? Rio? Crystal? Does anything actually exist outside of her Self?

Do you let fear pull you out of the experience?

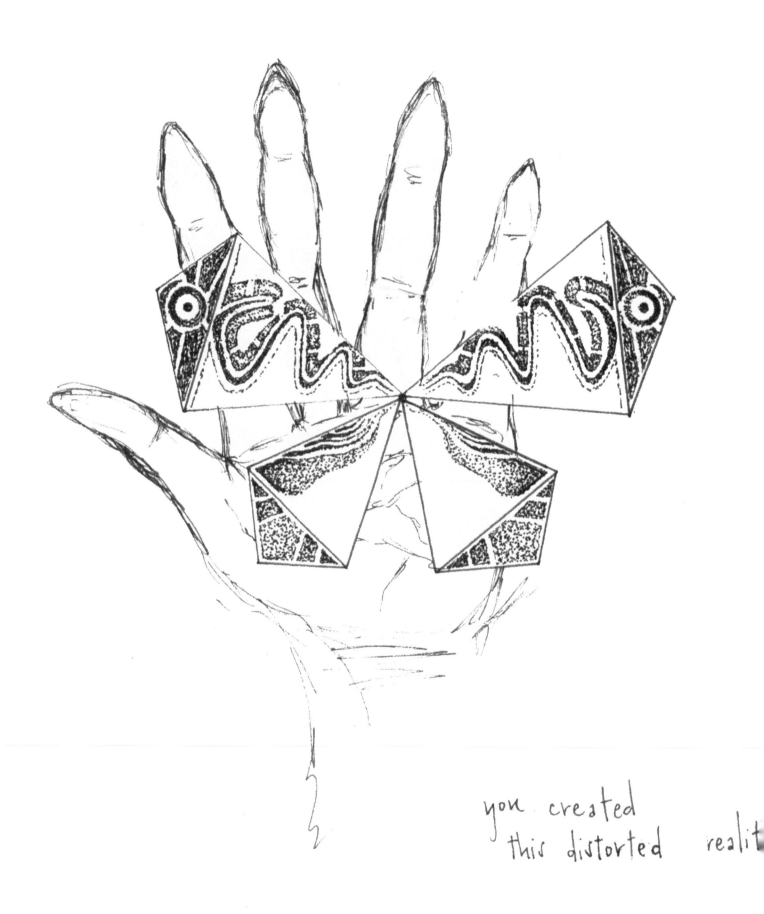

you created
this distorted realit

Control

The overwhelming sensations of bright colors and loud sounds drown out her mind again, and she fights to keep her eyes open, but fails. The body feels weak, and it half melts, half sinks into the sandy ground, cool as the heat rises.

Desertia has no choice but to surrender to the chaos as she is suddenly blasted through a tunnel of dimly lit stars, spiraling narrower. A small bright light grows larger as she approaches it, until it completely takes over the dark and leaves her standing atop the cloud she had been on only a couple nights ago camping with the city dwellers.

Familiar faces, the two androgynous beings, tall and slender, with overly excited smiles stare at her. One is tainted a cool blue, one purple. As if Life were a skipping tape, she relives the scene.

"You made it!" the blue being on the right shouts, the purple being clapping their hands. The abstract bodies run toward Desertia, their limbs morphing and wiggling with each step, and this time she does not move. The purple one hugs her tight, too tight, and she feels she might suffocate.

The body does not return the hug and she cannot ask for release. After they let go, the purple being asks, "Can you still not see me?"

The blue one laughs a short, harsh laugh. "Of course she can't, she is illusioned by some idea of 'self'." It waves its hand in front of her face, her eyes not moving. "See? We might as well be invisible."

"Do you think we should meet her there then? She must know we've arrived," the purple being asks.

Desertia wants to scream, to say anything, to let them know she can see them, but she is frozen, empty, completely out of touch with the body. The blue being brings their face close to hers, eyes like needles as they make direct eye contact. She cannot even blink.

She stares back at them with no other option, feeling uncomfortable in her own skin, insecure about what she may look like up close. Their irises are unavoidable and, as she accepts her lack of control, she begins to make out an image—her reflection.

It makes complete sense that she has no control over the body, the vessel she is in, because it is not hers. Another androgynous figure, with no appearance of sexual organs, stares at the pupils in front of her. She is tinted yellow and embodies similar facial characteristics as the two beings she has encountered.

Without the ability for words or movement, she can only communicate with her reflection through the mind, the voices in her head.

"You are in total control," the voice says, "You can escape at any time."

Think of all the connections you have made with people, animals, objects, etc.
Can you remember your connectedness to all things?

145

Reflection

The chanting ends, the silence pulling her out of the clouds and back into the sweat lodge.

The door opens, and she waits patiently for the next two stones. Ramón crawls out of the dome after saying a muffled prayer, and she feels relief in knowing she is not the only one who needs a break.

She waits for a few minutes, the heat completely gone from the dome, before she starts to wonder when the men will come back. Crawling clockwise to the exit, she pokes her head out to see the men sitting by the fire, staring into the flames with intense glares, as if to put it out with thought. Feeling her presence, Ramón looks over at her and, reading the expression of confusion on her face, he says, "That is all, my sister, five rounds, plus a warrior round."

Desertia recounts the stones, noticing four more since the fourth round. She wonders if she had fallen asleep or if he is playing mind games.

"Come, sit," Ramón says, waving her to the fire, "Tell me about your journey."

In an attempt to stand, she notices the body feeling weak, her legs shaking under her bodyweight. She stays low to the ground, moving slowly toward the fire. Ramón extends a cup of water to her, and she gulps it down, feeling every drip move through the esophagus, remembering the rocket ship she was just on, soaring through a spiraling universe. Nausea dominates her.

Finally, the body releases the dis-ease inside of her.

Ramón gets up quickly to support her, rubbing her back like a mother does a sleeping baby. Diga shovels sand over her mess, whispering a short prayer with each scoop.

The purge offers bliss, a relief, and she sips the water again. Ramón returns to his seat around the fire, Diga to his. Light headed, she gazes at the pile of sand, grateful to have released so much weight.

"The Truth can only flood a clear vessel. How are you feeling sister?" Ramón asks.

Tuning into the mental and physical body, she experiences feelings of bodily exhaustion, weakness. Mentally, she feels light, a heightened clarity.

"I am understanding the mind is not weighed down by gravity," she says finally.

"We get wiser when we're together. We get stronger. Not even gravity can stop us. We can escape it at any time," Ramón responds, staring directly into her eyes.

The body heats up and prickles run down her spine, the mind remembering what the voices in her head said just before her trance ended. Was it a coincidence that Ramón was now repeating the same words? She wonders if he can read her mind, or if his gift is to experience another's reality as if it were his own.

146

"Are you…" she fades out, unsure how to ask him without embarrassing her Self.

"Yes," he says after a moment. "That's correct."

Desertia does not say anything, not because she cannot think of the next thing to say or because she does not have the ability to speak, but because she does not feel it is necessary. Words are not necessary, only a waste of breath.

When she looks at him, he stares back. When she looks into the fire, he does too. The inner child is amused. She smiles at him, he returns an identical smile. She laughs awkwardly, he mimics. She stops, confused, he stops, appearing confused.

The game, at first playful, now becomes irritating. She wants it to end.

"Don't you see me, sister? I am merely a reflection of you, as we all are. We've been waiting for you to notice us," Ramón says.

She looks at Diga, who smiles sweetly at her, nodding.

Not fully grasping what he is saying or maybe just not wanting to accept his words, she feels the need to run, to escape, but what good will it do? Where will she go? The voices in her head tell her she cannot run from the Truth, as her internal GPS will always lead her back to it.

There are so many questions she wants to ask, so many things to say. Self-doubt prevents her from expressing it, to her Self or anyone else. She feels vulnerable, gullible, and, at the same time, believing fully what she is comprehending.

Desertia looks back to Ramón, "Yes, I see you. You are the beings from my vision, you are the voices in my head, you are me."

She does not know how to continue without questions. How? Why? Now what? Without her ever speaking them aloud, Ramón shrugs, one corner of his mouth rising, "Would you rather understand it all or live for the mystery?"

Her initial instinct is to know now, so she can live the rest of this Life understanding why she was chosen to survive. At the same time, she fears knowing, which may expose her to loneliness in oneness, being unified with all beings, and the death of curiosity, her drive and Life's force.

There is no possibility for connection with Truth that will leave her feeling complete. There is no Life after such a death of curiosity, as there would be no room for imagination, creation, or manifestation.

You may find your Self in one or more characters and stories, and I encourage you to look deeper…
Can you find your Self in all of them?

Journal Entry 9

Dear Moraine,

I feel obligated to feel love for all beings if they are all me, but I feel resentment. Was everyone in on this? Why did nobody tell me? But who is "everyone" if they are each reflections of my Self, each a part of Life?

What is the meaning of this necklace around my neck?

Life's sequence of events, guiding me from one person and place to the next, my next mentor, my next student. Have I just been talking to my Self this entire time?

The draw I experienced with Crystal, the connection I have to Rio, how can I sit with the idea that they are just copies of me?

Like my mirror reflection, dressing up for the city lights, it's so rare, if not impossible, I, or anyone else, ever see our Self. Photos, mirrors, water, the reflection always feeling so alien.

Even when I project outside of the body, watching this vessel sit in meditation or sleep, I cannot see the Self. The Self is not an external appearance, but an internal way of being. It cannot be seen, so I find deeper, more valuable connections in partnership and friendship, which can be seen, touched. Doesn't everyone?

That concept again. "Everyone."

What about those passerbys? Diga, who has said so few words in our short interaction. Even he was in on this secret before I was. Does he exist outside of those short moments together? Does he experience a life of autonomy and pleasure? Does he suffer?

Or is he just a copy of my Self, a gift for this occasion, created by me, for me?

My mind is frustrated by the Truth, which is the fact that I may never receive any of the answers I am looking for. Ramón may know, or he may not, but he may speak as though he does. If I were to absorb his knowledge, my perspective of this entire reality would be skewed—it would be his perspective.

And yet so many people, pre and post-pandemic, lived and live as sponges. Ideas, societal expectations, religious morals, fear, all connect back to one person.

If everyone is a reflection of my Self, then that one person was me, is me. Everyone can trace their suffering back to my Self. What a weight to hold!

For what reason did I bear the gift of healing and wisdom to these people then? Has healing and guiding others been nothing but a self-healing prophecy? Then how does it end? Is there an end? Maybe it is this.

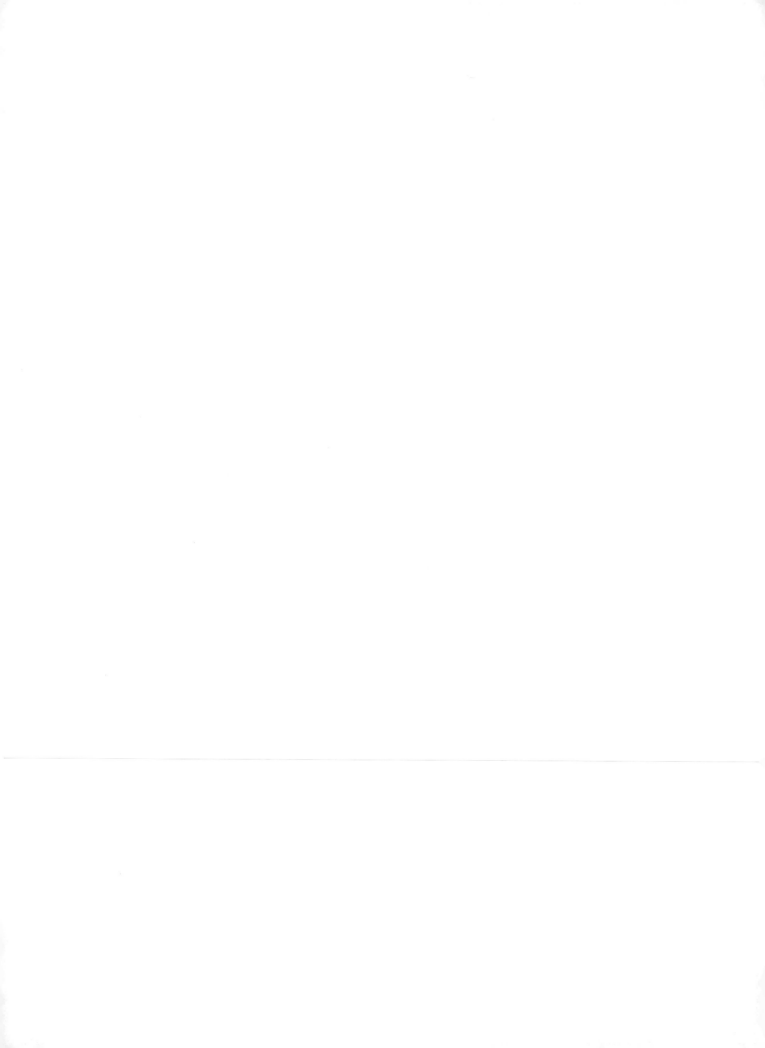

About the Author

Entrepreneur, coach, and artist, Chamomile Diddell is a vessel for guidance and intuitive offerings. She is a jack-of-all-trades, non-conformist, and world traveler, dabbling in every hobby and relishing in every experience she meets.

Regarded as an "old-soul", she creates many outlets for her to share the wisdom coming through her, including a luxury decluttering business; a spiritual mentorship program, The Journey to Self; art; and *Hello, Sweet Spirit*. Chamomile is also a certified reiki healer and intuitive tattoo artist.

For four years, she wandered North America and Southeast Asia participating in and organizing art exhibitions, mindfulness illustration workshops, and Southeast Asia's first art retreat.

It is her mission to expand the collective consciousness, beginning with her Self, so she seeks out healing and wisdom for her own conscious evolution. She shares this adopted and intuitive wisdom anyway the path presents itself to her

Hello, Sweet Spirit is a manifestation of this purpose, combining the art and experience from her journey as an offering to guide you on yours.

Check out www.hellosweetspirit.com for more offerings from Chamomile.

Printed in the USA
CPSIA information can be obtained
at www.ICGtesting.com
LVHW061929280923
757896LV00048B/63